D0428889

The Making of the Messiah, 2048

Gidon Rothstein

First published 2019

ISBN: 978-1-56871-673-2

Published by
Targum Publishers
Shlomo ben Yosef 131a/1
Jerusalem 9380581
editor@targumpublishers.com

Distributed by
Ktav Publishers & Distributors Inc.
527 Empire Blvd.
Brooklyn, NY 11225-3121
Tel: 718-972-5449, 201-963-9524
Fax: 718-972-6307, 201-963-0102
www.ktav.com

Printed in Israel

Funeral Announcement: Sar Shalom, Messiah, King of Israel

With sadness and submission to the Judge of All Truth, the grieving Palace announces the passing to the next world of His Late Majesty, Light of All Israel, Redeemer of the World, King Sar Shalom. The funeral will take place, Gd willing, on Wednesday, 25 Nisan, 5808 – April 8, 2048 by the world's calendar – in the courtyard to the Kotel, the Old Western Wall, at 9AM.

Traffic Congestion Warning, Monday 23 Nisan Through Tuesday, 1 Iyyar

The Municipal Police of Jerusalem alerts the public to extraordinary congestion for the coming days. The grieving Palace asks us to stress how much they (and we) value and welcome any and all who feel moved to pay last respects to our dear departed Messiah. At the same time as we encourage attendance at the funeral procession and/or week of mourning, we would be remiss if we did not inform the public – Jerusalem residents and not – about coming days.

We expect and hope a million extra people to be in the city on Wednesday, to accompany the bier from the Kotel to the Mount of Olives. Road closure maps are attached, as are expected interruptions or slowdowns in public transportation. With apologies to all residents, who bear sudden influxes around holidays, too.

Ticketed attendees to the funeral itself must budget for delays as they time their arrival at the security check booths. We will do our best to screen at the minimum, will remind our officers of the many weapons His Late Majesty's force field detects, and to check for the lighter weapons with all possible dispatch.

Following the funeral and procession, snarls will likely continue throughout the week of mourning, to a still noticeable extent, particularly in the blocks around the Palace, where groups will be gathered to await entry for condolence calls.

May we all be comforted soon, and we thank you in advance for your good-spirited cooperation during these challenging times.

Grieving Palace Announcement 17: Funeral Service, Tentative Schedule

Funeral services for His Late Majesty will be broadcast on screens in public places throughout the country, as well as your usual online servers. For ease of planning, the grieving Palace publishes the current tentative schedule.

The Palace also asks the public's indulgence for what might seem a disrespectfully sparse slate of speakers. His Late Majesty specifically insisted on a limited program, to avoid burdening those who wish to attend or watch what he only grudgingly conceded would be an historic event. The Palace has allowed our Office of Palace Announcements to reveal the heated discussions with his family, where His Late Majesty threatened to insist on no eulogies, were they unable to reach a compromise.

The family has also consulted with our esteemed rabbis at the Sanhedrin and our Temple leadership, who advised on and approved the lineup; given the time constraints His Late Majesty demanded, we expect the program to last between sixty and ninety-five minutes. On behalf of all involved, we at the Office of Palace Announcements beg the public's and His Late Majesty's forgiveness for mistakes or omissions, ask we be given the benefit of the doubt on errors at this difficult time.

We remind you of the possibility of last-minute changes and emergencies. Barring any, the proceedings will open at 9AM with a Psalm read by His Late Majesty's elementary school classmate, Rabbi Amittai Guvrin, emeritus assistant head of the Sanhedrin.

Eulogies will follow, by:

His Late Majesty's longtime assistant/ Chief of Staff, Ms. Shani Feinbaum;

Our honored *nasi,* Head of the Sanhedrin, Rabbi Yohanan Attarah;

His Most Esteemed High Priest Pinhas;

His Late Majesty's lifelong friend Ben Silverstein;

Princess Jo;

Concluding with *E-l Malei*, the memorial prayer, sung by Head Levi Amram b. Yitzhar.

The family apologizes to the many world leaders they are unable to ask to speak. They and all Israel are honored by the presence of such august dignitaries. His Late Majesty treasured his relationships with peers across the world, friends he relished seeing at the annual summits. To single out any for special attention would dishonor the rest, and there is not time for all to speak. Immediately after the opening Psalm, we will acknowledge by name the representatives of each government, to thank all who made it to Jerusalem on this extremely short notice.

Following the Memorial prayer, His Late Majesty himself selected the eight longest-serving members of his private guard to carry the bier to the Mount of Olives. The route, with locations of the seven stops, is attached. At each stop, there will be time for brief reminiscences. Those who wish to enter the lottery to represent the public with remarks at any stop should please fill out the entry form at MyMessiahwasking.com.

The family assures the public they will be as touched by those whose spirit moves them to line the route to the burial as by those who win the lottery to attend the funeral. They remind the public of His Late Majesty's fondness for John Milton's words, "They also serve who only stand and wait." The public will do the grieving royal family a further favor by sharing any personal stories of His Late Majesty at MyMessiahwasking.com. All submissions will be read, a sample brought to the family daily.

May we all soon see the fullest comfort of those awaiting the Resurrection of the Dead, when we will all be reunited with our lost loved ones, and with His Late Majesty.

ABC NEWS Special Report, 8AM, Monday April 6, 2048: Who Was the Messiah?

Transcript prepared by: Journalism intern Sam Smith

Welcome back to ABC News, where we bring you the world, before anyone else. In our moment to moment times, make sure ABC comes straight to your inbox, to keep you ahead, on top, in control. Here now, Tilda Anchor with a special report.

Hello, everyone, I'm Tilda Anchor, and it is my sorrowful duty to report the death of the man Israelis call Messiah. King Sar Shalom has lost his battle with very old age and the illnesses which come with. We thank Reuters for sharing that tidbit, they share their Israeli correspondent with us, and turn now to our own Shalinda Karujikani, Central Asia correspondent. Shalinda, who *was* Sar Shalom of Israel?

Thanks, Tilda, pleasure to work with you again. Born Yuri Hyrikov in Kyiv – my neck of the woods, reportorially speaking, is why I know the man so well, I've been covering him almost from the start – the man the world would come to know as Sar Shalom, Hebrew for prince of peace, moved to Israel at seventeen. He often told interviewers the draft made him do it, here's a clip to help those of you who, like me, struggle to put a face to an uncommon name. It's from soon after he was elected Prime Minister, a testament to how much his features stayed the same as he aged.

"I was in high school, usual disrespect for authority, thought to myself, no way am I letting apparatchiks or oligarchs cost me my leg or life. If I had to suffer anything like that, I was determined it would be for a cause I cared about. Ukraine birthed me, raised me, I enjoyed most of my time there. Not enough to bear those risks."

Drafted into the Israeli infantry after his citizenship cleared, Yuri climbed the ladder double time, pulled ever upwards by superiors who spotted his leadership skills, jostled for the bragging rights on who had given him his crucial boost. The cherry on top came at the Battle of the Bosporus, during the second Israeli-Turkish war. The Medal of Honor citation quoted friends and captured foes, who agreed he had single-handedly turned the tide, his disregard for personal safety an inspiration to his fellow soldiers. The medal panel of inquiry accepted the experts' estimates he had saved thousands of soldiers' lives on each side by shortening the battle.

Back from the war, the toast of the town opted out of a military career, perhaps his low point in the eyes of public opinion. Back then, Israelis held their heroes to a rigid expected path, stay in the Army until you find out you either are or are not going to be Chief of Staff, only then transition to politics and financial security.

His early withdrawal caused a nose dive in the polls, no one likes the guy who reaches for the golden ring too soon. The numbers bounced back only when he rented the patent for his force field – the first economically viable large-scale protection device, he would say to anyone who would listen – to the Israeli Government for a G-7 salary, as if he headed a minor department of the Defense Ministry.

The percentage he took from rentals to other nations made him the richest man on earth, yet sources in the Ministry tell me of the awe in which he was held for having given up unimaginable further wealth had had he kept the company private. How much more he could have made had he not insisted all installations of the force field employ only Israelis.

One year after installation, terrorist and rocket attacks reduced to an easily policed trickle, the prime minister, Robert Friedman, insisted Hyrikov take over, said it was a joke for him to pretend to run the country when "Young Yuri," as the press dubbed him, was the reason for the nation's prosperity and security.

Elevated into office by acclaim, he called elections, insisted the people needed a say in who served as their leader. Knesset – sorry, that was the Parliament at the time, disbanded these many years he has been king – Leaders of the Knesset countered by placing his name at the top of each party's list. Voters could weigh in on the party that would staff his government, no one was willing to have anyone else as PM.

Thanks, Shalinda, sorry to cut you off, I'm sure we'll be coming back to you in the hours and days to come. Right now, we have a vital update from Erin Draymond, at JFK.

Tilda, as you can see on your split screens, here at JFK, at Newark Liberty and airports in Chicago, Boston, and LA, we have thousands scrambling to get to Israel for the funeral. Airline help desks tell us they had prepared for a spike, had scheduled some extra emergency flights, are still overwhelmed, people having locked in tickets from as soon as they heard of doctors heading to the Palace, and no one's cancelling.

The airlines are re-routing flights, the Israeli government is reopening airports like Sde Dov, rumors are floating around they might bulldoze emergency strips in Gush Etzion, a bloc of towns to the southeast of Jerusalem, to handle some of the traffic. Sar Shalom has left a tidy little death benefit for airlines servicing the country, many of whom have scheduled conference calls to revise quarterly estimates upward. US companies know not to be accused of lowballing expectations to pad their own accounts, profit on the uptick of a surprise higher tally.

"Revise significantly upward," one publicist told me, off the record.

Yes, thank you, Tilda, I see it. Ladies and gentlemen, on your screens, we have footage from my colleagues Angela Carinyani, Lee Shu-kin, Helena Parikhar, and Tim Cassidy at the airports in Los Angeles, Chicago, Miami, and Boston. It's not just New Yorkers rushing to Jerusalem, as you can see.

Erin, sorry, let's hit pause for a moment; Israeli government censors have just cleared us to announce the Royal Family has decided to delay the funeral a day, to Wednesday, in surrender to the reality of the limitations of their travel infrastructure, their lack of landing strips for the flights headed their way, particularly those of heads or representatives of governments.

"We are determined those who wish to pay Our Late Majesty final respects should be able to reach Jerusalem comfortably on and in time," said Palace spokesperson Tallulah Omer.

As longstanding Jerusalem custom prohibits any body staying in the city overnight, His Late Majesty's bier was taken out before nightfall, will spend the next thirty-six hours circuiting the country by train and limousine. Added plus: Israelis will be able to pay respects without further clogging the capital or the roads, or take extra time from work. The caravan will move slowly, we are told, providing many opportunities to walk behind the body, recite the traditional Psalms. Ok, back to you, Erin.

Thanks, Tilda, one last note, a woman here at the airport refused to go on camera, told me, "I always thought I'd see him one more time. You know a man's getting old, you know no one's immune to death, some part of your brain fools you, says, hey, he's the Messiah, he'll always be there. For me, the shock of hearing the word death in the same sentence as King Sar Shalom told me I had to be there, to let him and his family know how much we cared, how much it meant to us he made Israel strong and invulnerable."

That's the way some Jews are seeing it. For ABC News, at JFK, I'm Erin Draymond.

Great work, Erin, thanks. We're just getting our first list of dignitaries heading there. The heads of state of Russia, China, France, India, UK, Brazil, and Canada are all on their way to Israel, please check our ticker often, the list is sure to grow today and tomorrow, oh, this just in, the German Chancellor, and Secretary of State Dustin Culmember will represent the US. For a quick analysis, we go to Adnan Khashalli, at our Middle East desk.

Tilda, a not unexpected choice, will still give fodder to the President and Vice President's political opponents. The President can point to Congress' refusal to suspend the docket, with crucial bills up for a vote in coming days. They've given him cover to say he can't get away, has to be in the trenches making sure his bills pass.

It's also a little convenient, leading some to suggest it's a bipartisan effort by Congress, to help the President retaliate a bit for Sar Shalom's usurping the US role on the world stage. Starting from when the G-8 insisted on expanding to G-9, then made Israel the permanent host, relations with the US have frosted for more than a decade. Successive presidents have tried to couch it as a matter of principle, grousing about the lack of freedoms in a theocratic monarchy.

The Royal family has refused to be drawn into unpleasantness. The Palace has issued a statement thanking all those coming, and single out Secretary Culmember, praising him for the special relationship he had with His Late

Majesty. Insult deflected, ball back in the US court. And back to you, Tilda.

Appreciate it, Adnan, now our mental health correspondent, Dr. Filomena Grantland.

Thanks, Tilda, and thank you to ABC News/Entertainment for giving me a moment here to talk about some of the issues sure to arise in coming weeks. I'm hearing from clients here in the States worried the new king might end the force field rental program; will all of us be thrown back into a world of war and violence?

Jews outside Israel (full disclosure: I converted thirty years ago, when I married my first husband, although I returned to the Church when we divorced) may find themselves with new guilt over their failure to join what many view as the Messianic era. Israelis will struggle with the unexpected dilemma of how to live without the man they thought had brought the end of history.

Not for now, I suppose, but there's reason to wonder about the mental state of the new king as well, the young Hazoniyah. What's it like to step into those shoes, we might wonder. I'd hate to be *his* mental health advisor, that'd be quite the task.

In whichever group you belong, two quick pieces of advice: consult *your* mental health professional, it's why we're here, and focus away from yourself. Studies show thinking of others short-circuits our perseverations – sorry, thanks, professional hazard, it means obsessing.

Over the coming uncertain days, I'm saying, look for people who have it worse. Think of this grieving family, forced to undergo this most private moment in this most public way. The experienced public servants of the group, the widow, Daughter Yeho'adan or Jo, and the new king, they're pros, look for the littlest cracks in their composure, they'll tell you a great deal. We'll especially want to track the crown prince's transition to the throne. Only time will tell.

Thanks, Fiona, sorry, Filomena. Heh-heh, looks like I'm a bit off my game, I guess it's some of those worries you were highlighting. This concludes our ABC News/Entertainment special report, we don't want to give anyone reason to think we're trying to dump information on you, hide it under the cover of a bunch of correspondents you'll never see again, can't tell apart without a scorecard. We all look the same, our Insta-Snappers are telling us, it's basically a talking head throwing information at you.

We apologize. We here at ABC are focused on your experience as a viewer, and know you prefer the bare bones, left to find the rest yourselves. We thought our loyal news aficionados would want as much background as we could provide, thought chopping it into parts, explained by experts in each field, would make it easier to digest.

We hear you, though, keep sending those comments, sorry, I mean keep Snapping at us. In deference to your preferences, ABC is moving, as we speak, to centralize our coverage. Starting with the funeral, we will have one correspondent anchoring all our Israel news, our own Rachel Tucker, doing us all a favor by stepping back in front of the camera. Join us for the comfort of again hearing "Rachel Tucker, ABC News, Jerusalem."

For younger viewers who do not know our behind the scenes people – and please do think about taking the time to meet our behind the scenes crews, they're all featured at our home site, definitely reward a look – we're flashing her info on the ticker right now, her thirty year membership in the ABC family.

Her time in Israel back when the kingdom was young gives her an insight and set of contacts we are confident will translate into coverage you will find must-see. A treat, you'll see.

On behalf of Shalinda, Erin, and Adnan, our affiliates across the country, Angela, Shu-kin, Helen, and Tim, I'm Tilda Anchor, thanking you for choosing ABC News. Back to our smash reality hit, *24 Hours In A Casket*!

FORBES PLUS BREAKING TIP, 10:12AM, MONDAY, APRIL 6, 2048

You want the money, we show you how to make it; congratulations, *FORBES PLUS* Subscriber, we're here today with another dividend off your investment in *FORBES PLUS,* your eighty-seventh tip of the year. This latest is rated triple gold; while of course past results are no guarantee of future performance, our triple gold recommendations have generated returns 132% better than market, over one, three, and five-year horizons (those numbers thanks to outside evaluator J.D. Power and Associates). Stick with *FORBES PLUS,* we'll keep you ringing the register, adding to the till.

Today's tip: The Messiah's death, ideas for leverage from Africa/Asia specialist, Misawi Zengote. Here he is.

Ok, investor buddies, Messiahs don't die every day, and the markets notice, it doesn't matter if only twelve million or all twelve billion of the world's people thought of him that way. As our motto goes here at *FORBES PLUS* – say it with me, loud, if the smell of money moves you – CHANGE SPELLS OPPORTUNITY.

As long as you know the type of change headed your way, place your bets where they'll do the most good, you'll be coming out way ahead (Legal disclosure: Misawi Zengote, members of his team, and many *FORBES* staff *will* buy stocks in line with these recommendations. As per *FORBES* policy, all who buy commit to own for six months, to make sure our readers know we're not puffing up the market to grab a quick profit and leave you in the lurch.)

The key lies in putting your chips down on sectors where he mattered. Expect a dip in all stocks with a significant component of Israeli business, over the uncertainty about the new king and country's future. No one knows if the son will be able to fill the shoes of *this* father, however much training and preparation he's had. It's a worry to keep in mind.

Except no nation is one person, we expect a recovery as the country finds its way, with or without the heir. You can bet on the dip *and* the recovery, if you time it right.

That concludes the generality portion of our program, let's tussle with some specifics. Had this Messiah conquered the whole world, it'd be hard to pick a play, all the markets would be jittery, every industry, company, and country looking for their new normal. Sar Shalom made it easier, Israel's pretty small, its economic dominance relies on a narrow range of businesses, the force field and its support industries.

Sadly, few of us can invest directly in Force Field, Inc. Kidding; there is no Force Field, Inc., I know that. I meant the seventeen companies who jointly own it, all listed on the Tel Aviv Exchange, and only current citizen-residents of Israel can buy shares on the Exchange.

Be careful, some people hear Israeli, think it's enough to be Jewish. I know people who have *converted* thinking it will buy them access – don't get me started, we're here to talk about the money part, not the crazy part, it's a six month process, minimum – then found out it's a matter of residence, not religion.

There *are* rumors of Israelis who will buy for you. It could work, Tel Aviv looks poised for a break in growth as the country pauses to right itself. If you're thinking of it – and *FORBES PLUS* absolutely does not and cannot condone law-breaking; many of our tips come from government sources, the spigot would shut tight the instant anyone in government thought we promote breaking their laws – getting caught will wipe out whatever gains you made and more, for you and whoever serves as your stand-in.

Also jail time, unless you stay away from all 107 countries with extradition treaties with Israel. Including, of course, the United States. The likelihood of being caught has risen, too, Israeli security has been cracking down since the late king's illness, anticipating such vulture investing. At the most practical level, it means you have to include the indemnity fee for the stand-in as part of your investment costs. Sure, it'll be returned when you sell safely, if you do.

We at *FORBES PLUS* pride ourselves on sharing *innovative* ideas, the ones your run of the mill advisor would never come up with. Anyone can notice the Tel Aviv Stock Exchange has beaten the indexes each of the past fifteen years. You pay us to ferret out the value plays you can't find on your own, and we work hard to earn and keep your loyalty.

We have what we believe is an excellent alternative, the Temple Grounds, trades on the NASDAQ for anyone to buy. Look it up, you won't understand why I have to defend it as much as I'm about to until you know what it is. I'll wait.

I know, now you think I'm crazy, how could a lightly traded, five-store chain of coffee shops produce the kind of return to justify a *FORBES PLUS* Breaking Tip? Yeah, yeah, don't Insta-Snap at me, read to the end, people. Savvy investors don't rush to judgment, or else they never end up as rich as they could have. Or as wise, if that interests you.

First point: Flagship store is a close walk to the funeral site, means foot traffic will skyrocket in coming days. Remember their motto, closest cuisine, coffee, and comfort to the Temple. People with tickets will stop on their way to carb load, or on the way back for comfort food; some percentage of people who didn't get tickets will decide to watch the proceedings from as close as they can get; and security details for funeral prep, cleanup, will drop in for a muffin, bagel, and coffee before, during, and after their shifts.

It's a skip and a jump from the palace, it'll be swamped the week of mourning, too.

They should have a longer term bump from the national recovery period psychologists predict. You get used to a Messiah smoothing your life, it can be hard to let him go, lots of people will be overwhelmed. Some will go for traditional therapy, sure, others will insist they can do it on the cheap, and The Temple Grounds aggressively markets their therapist/ baristas. Twenty bucks on food and a schmooze beats two hundred for what's often no better.

FORBES predicts they'll double net profits this quarter. When those numbers come out, fools will rush in, we'll get out [note: we're telling you this up front, don't blame us when we sell faster than six months], because they can't keep it up beyond a quarter. Sure, their guidance for analysts talks about starting a catering business, expansion to places like Seattle, Portland, Rome, and other high-stress, high-therapy cities. *FORBES PLUS* doesn't see it translating, therapy's culture-specific, especially the semi-pro kind. Buy the stock, hold it for the bump after their next earnings report, and sell.

ABC News/Entertainment, Meeting Summary, No. AZF-342967

April 4, 2048, 12;17pm

From: Leanne Conover, President, ABC News/Entertainment

To: Ryan Williamson III, Sr. Vice President for News

Topic: Winning the Damn Funeral

Ryan, sorry to be as formal as to time-stamp, official-server dispatch this. You know how it is at ABC these days, CYA, make a pixel trail, nail down the evidence I did my job within reasonable expectations. In case anything goes south.

Not that I'm expecting it, of course not. It's the rules, I have to give you a chance to correct any misimpressions from our last conversation. I know, rules are made to be broken, and usually we ignore this one. Right now, I'm getting too much heat, it's time to work by the book, if we all do, we'll all come out fine.

Background: In our conversation, I reminded you of our past three underperforming quarters, an unacceptable situation for the khakis upstairs. They're getting antsy, are not willing to wait much longer for us to turn this around. They pull out the boot, it won't be me on the receiving end, I've got a mortgage, boat, and three exes to support. And their kids.

Bottom line, if you want to be around two quarters from now, we better do better. Step one is this memo, for you to initial or edit and then initial. Protects us both, gives you a chance to object to whichever parts you think I got wrong. Thanks, buddy.

Conversation Recap: I called you in, we agreed your division is a disaster. Without a ten GRPs boost in the short term, twenty within six months, it will clearly be house-cleaning time. Increased use by current viewers, finding a way to have them check in ten times a day rather than five, might get us a quarter of the way, although we agree that market's pretty saturated.

Brings us to Wednesday's funeral, a chance at a new audience, people drawn in by the death to maybe start following Israel again. We connect the name ABC in their minds to riveting TV from Israel, we've done ourselves a favor. Quite the nut to crack, we agreed, Americans who follow other countries is the smallest of niches right now.

The Idea: That's why I told you to send Rachel Tucker. There, you have it in writing, I made the decision, if she messes up, you're off the hook. Knowing you, you probably think I've fallen into your trap, put my head on the chopping block, opened the door for you when I get canned. Not that you doubt Rachel, I know, you doubt *anyone* can pull this off, you think I've made the wrong choice on how to turn this all around.

Caution: Don't be too sure of yourself. First, never bet against Rachel Tucker, she's held on in this young person's world – she's in her fifties, I don't know if you realize – she's adapted, changed, she's a fighter. And she knows Israel, you wouldn't know it from casual conversation, but at late-night office parties, it comes out.

Yes, she always acts like she put it behind her completely when she left there twenty years ago, except she's slipped, shown insight into what's going on you can only have if you spend your middle of the night wakeups catching up on the news, scrolling multiple sites for various perspectives. I don't know why she does it, I just know she's got unfinished business. Good for us, means she's ready to hit the ground running.

And if I'm wrong? Well, sorry, still not great for you, everyone around here knows you're my guy; I do well, you do well, you do well, I get the credit. I go down, you're not far behind, that's not a threat, I won't have to lift a finger or an eyebrow, it's what happens to proteges when the big boss reaches the end of the road.

Now that I have this in writing, by the way, when she goes gangbusters, as I'm betting, it's all me, baby, all me.

Action Plan: Here's the part that's on you: she's put out this whole narrative about how she'll never go back there, never go in front of the cameras again, never, blah, blah, blah, etc. Which means she's going to put up the biggest resistance you've ever seen. Who refuses a shot at on-air time? She will, I'm telling you.

You need to rev her engines, be sure she's determined to knock this one outta the park. Unless her whole head is in the game, well, you can take a horse to water and all that.

Plan ahead: she'll say she hasn't been in front of a camera in a decade; needs to drop the "producer's ten," and no diet will take it off fast enough; signed away her rights to re-enter last time she left, some misunderstanding with the authorities (that's true, call our immigration guys, I bet it's an hour's conversation with some bureaucrat over there, $5000 fine or something).

Shepherd her past all of it, we need her all-in, excited to go gangbusters, whatever rah-rah you find. And still, I think you'll need a little stick, it's why I'm asking you and not Shirley. She'd never use enough stick, they're too close. Besides, you hand it off to Shirley, I'd start wondering why I need you on a VP salary when I get the same from her at Exec Producer rates.

The Stick: My impression is – this is only a suggestion, but if you don't take it and don't succeed, well, um – the college tuition clause is why Rachel's still with us. She has a son with two years left at Wharton, she can't cover it herself, who can? Should get her attention.

Strategizing Her Broadcasts: Remember to tell her to soft-pedal the Messiah part, our viewers don't want to hear that crap, it's why our Israel coverage dried up years ago. Not to speak ill of the dead, but how this Sar Shalom thought a Christian country would tolerate a Jew showing up as Messiah is beyond me.

Course, it's not his problem anymore, it's ours. Or, really, Rachel's. She can't give viewers a whiff she buys into the craziness, or she's toast, and so are we. To remind you: we have *one shot* – anyone we turn off is never coming back, so do it right the first time. Hash out an approach, something the Israelis won't flag, winks at viewers, tells them she's in on it. Maybe anytime she should say "Messiah," we hear "the man Israelis thought of as Messiah," you know?

Make it like an anthropological study of a group of crazies you can't ever let know you've decided are crazies. They *think* they've lost a Messiah, what happens? Without tipping off the Israelis or being as dry as a real anthropological study, who wants to watch or hear an anthropological study? Like, build enough background to put viewers in Israelis' shoes, how they've followed this guy since his first election in 2020, almost thirty years in power, twenty-three as king, they're still mad for him. Viewers will latch on right away, they're smart, they'll want to know how he survived the disaster of '24, why Israelis didn't throw the bums out every four years. Show 'em a success, they'll be mad it wasn't them, will want to know how it went different over there.

Or maybe you and she come up with a better angle, something more personal? She used to live there, she'll know how to make it touching.

Presentation Counts: Last point, as I'm thinking, maybe Shirley *should* join your discussion after you've told Rachel the basics. No black mark on you, there's some stuff she might want to say woman to woman, we don't want a lawsuit. We need her to remind Rachel of industry expectations these days for on-air women, Spanx, a haircut, a better dye job.

Don't hyperventilate, this is business, not personal preferences or harassment, I can hear the wheels turning in your head, is this enough to report me. It's not, I've been in this business a long time. *I* think she looks great, I'd date her in a second if not for Internal Affairs, wouldn't say a word if she weren't going on camera.

The industry is what it is, we have to work within the limits, give our viewers what they demand. I can't wear whatever I want, you can't what you want, nobody can, and none of us has millions of people watching. Well, we hope it'll be millions.

Point is, no other anchor weighs over 120, has unstyled hair, we need her back up to accepted professional standards in her field. Courts have agreed, over and over, it's not our job to fall on our swords to educate viewers about how superficial all that is.

Ok, that's what I've got. I know, more direct than usual, maybe even confrontational. Sorry, time crunch, I can't take an hour to clear my head, an hour to write it, another hour to edit it into a more soft-spoken version, whittle it down to the usual style.

Because we need her on the next flight or we lose the funeral, we lose the funeral we all start circling the unemployment drain. You know I'm rooting for you, initial you've read it, please, send it back. Unless you have issues, comments, parts you want to review together.

Thanks.

INITIALED: RW

FORBES PLUS Special Edition: Business Owner Rebuttal

You want the money, we show you how to make it.

And we let you know when there's questions about our recommendations. Hey, *FORBES PLUS* subscribers, Misawi Zengote here, with an addendum to our buy and sell recommendation on The Temple Grounds. About an hour after we sent out our tip, I received an irate call from chain founder/CEO) Reuven HaOzer. The law requires *FORBES PLUS* to share his view.

"Mr. Zengote, ok Misawi, if you'll call me Reuven, no, it's three syllables, 'Re' as in reverse, 'oo' like 'moo', and 'ven,' like vane, vain, or vein. I'm obviously flattered, you build something, you always want outside interest, I admit it's part of why I listed on NASDAQ, I'm not going to lie, my wildest dreams *did* include headlines about an historic, record-breaking surge of trading in Temple Grounds stock. It's why I follow alerts like *FORBES PLUS,* you guys do a great job.

"Problem is, now's not the time, much as I'd love to have your subscribers as investors. I don't want your readers set up for a fall. All of your readers who decide the Temple Grounds are a good long-term play, *them* I'm happy to have, I think our best is yet to come.

"We *do* expect a big short-term surge in revenue, you've got that exactly right, although I say it with no glee, none of us takes any pleasure in benefitting from His Late Majesty's passing. At the same time, I think you've missed the challenges of those same months, exaggerated how much increased *profit* we can expect.

"Take staffing, for one example: people don't find therapist/baristas when they come in, they'll stop coming. We pride ourselves on the training they undergo, it takes us thirteen weeks to certify them, a twenty hour course just to qualify as trainees. People don't do that unless we guarantee six months of regular shifts. The short-term uptick in business is going to cost us longer term, is my point. If I instead siphon existing staff from other stores, I still have to pay extra shifts and the commuting premium.

"Suppliers, same deal. They're not going to let me up my orders on coffee, flour, sugar, milk, for only a month or two – they have to ramp up production to meet my needs, they're not going to want to find themselves with expensive excess capacity as soon as the mourning passes. I'm saying, with the wind in our sails comes drag readers should factor in.

"Last point, and please don't – you or your readers – think I'm being modest here, it's not one of my strengths. Juggling all these new balls will be mostly my problem, like the really early days, when I had the one store, didn't know half the mistakes I was making, business revved up faster than I dreamed it could, faster than any of my mentors anticipated.

"Imagine a first-time business owner scrambling to learn on the fly, for ten times as many people as expected. It was skin of the teeth, I was blowing investors' money almost as fast as it came in. Over time, sure, I got a handle on it, all the angel investors who stuck it out came away very happy. *My* best bet is the same will be true here; buy and hold, a year at least, I believe we'll do well by you.

"Let's give your readers an example, make it real: Over the next thirty-six hours, I have to figure out who has to staff the store, when all my people want to be at the funeral. Yeah, I've got screens in the shop, probably a better view than most seats, and if the commentary's any good, more insight, too. Still, wouldn't you want to be there?

"Obvious answer is stagger shifts, except the time to come up and down from the Kotel, sorry, I mean Old Wailing Wall, has lots of waste. I don't have the better solution, yet; it's not like I can trade missing this one for the next once-in-history event.

"We'll work it out, I'm not complaining, Misawi, I'm trying to help your readers see the whole picture. We'd *love FORBES PLUS* readers to join our little endeavor, my Investor Relations people would kill me if I didn't say that, and it's true, we in our little world know you tap into the kinds of people who know how to back the horse of the future. As long as you remember we're not the horse of the present."

Don't believe him, folks, hyper-caution and hyper-honesty are the rage in

Israel these days, the culture expects a million percent trustworthiness from their businesspersons. Customers in the five major cities in Israel will walk an extra five blocks to patronize a store they know meets their ethical standards, pay up to fifteen percent more. Part of the new cool, warts front and center, everyone knows exactly what they're risking.

My point is, take Reuven HaOzer seriously, then take this seriously: The Temple Grounds has a proven track record, has never missed a guidance on earnings, has opened five franchises in twenty years, ignored the frenzies, avoided the catastrophes of overexpansion. His marker is steady growth and a solid balance sheet. Like he says, a pretty sure bet long-term.

I'm betting (full disclosure: a million dollars, and I commit to selling within a week of their next quarterly, although I retain the right to buy back in, depending on developments) these next few weeks will take them to a new level. One you'll want to have joined me in joining.

Jack Tucker Email, Marked Urgent

Mom,

I got your call, called you back, saw you left a voice message. I think we've discussed my preference you not force me to use the voicemail system. I'd go on about it but I did listen, and I know you have more urgent things on your plate. Before anything else, I'm sorry the bastards are putting you in this position, really I am. You've done everything you could to give them more than value for their contract, I'm always amazed you produce such great shows. How many anchors move to directing and producing so seamlessly? Not a lot, and I don't want you to think I don't see it, even if they never admit it to you. Tough not to be appreciated, I know.

And I *do* appreciate you, I know how hard I would find a life without you at your job, paying my way in life. I think I know what a sacrifice I'm asking you to make, although you've always made this Israel thing a big mystery, tells me it must be something huge. And still.

Without a college degree, where am I in today's world? *Please* don't say anything about state or city schools, or bootstraps, either. Those days are gone, Mom, and you sound old and naïve when you say anything else. I'd love to be able to say: hey, you did the single mother thing for twenty years, I'm safely launched, congratulations, it's time for you to do you.

Sorry, it's not, not yet. And with the finish line so close, do you want to blow it over some incident in Israel from when I was a baby? You go there, the contract's safe, however you do. We both know you've always done me the favor of making my safety your top priority.

I *do* appreciate it, I just need it for a little longer.

Thanks, Mom, love ya, Jack

FOIA-Requested Internal SEC Memo: Market Manipulation Investigation

From: Zane Thomas, Chairman, Securities Exchange Commission

To: Charles McPike, Senior Staff, Division of Enforcement.

Chuck, attached is my memory of my half of our conversation, please review for errors or omissions. I'd like your comments and corrections, with your version of your half for my edits, within twenty-four hours, please, barring extraordinary circumstances.

Also, Chuck, a favor, this Temple Grounds thing came across my desk, look into it, will you? Stock's up 72 percent since the funeral was announced, trips the automated warning. I know there was a *FORBES PLUS* tip, we both know those guys at *FORBES wish* they could spark movement like that. Marketing's dreams, anyway. I know it's a tiny cap, you're thinking who would waste time manipulating it?

Still, 72 percent is a great return, and besides, why's a chain of *five* coffee shops in *Israel* listed at all? Five coffee shops, are you kidding me? I wouldn't have been sure we'd *incorporate* an operation that small, let alone let it go public.

I know, founder's American, could be nostalgia, point of pride, show the folks back home, look at me, I made it. Or give them the opportunity to invest by keeping it off the Tel Aviv exchange, yep, I know all of it.

Still, start down a shaky road, multiple cans of worms open. The people he wanted to do a favor, maybe they sold him on a pump and dump scheme. Or don't sell, buy, a ton, feed a bump, wait for it to drop back, original price is fine with them. Or some other scam I haven't thought of, its your job to figure it out.

Figure it out, please.

Also, this HaOzer, the owner, he's a distant cousin of a muckety-muck I cannot name, lawyers love using memos like these to prove preferential or overzealous treatment. This unnamed "investor" gave him a chunk of seed money in an early round. This friend of ours, if you know whom I mean, has been thinking of moving up in the world, taking a more public role, doesn't want this to come back to haunt him.

He's asked me, hush hush, to clear the Temple Grounds, make sure nothing about it will bring him grief down the road. Would help us a lot if someone in high places owed us, especially with the portfolio he's amassed of favors owed him. A powerful protector in these times is a necessity, when nobody thinks we SEC do anything anymore, what with how few lawsuits we file, how few fines we collect. Is it our fault businesspeople have gotten cleaner? Or smarter?

Yes, *FORBES* did include HaOzer in 60 Under 60, provides no defense for the stock price, none of those lists correlate, 40 Under 40, 50 Under 50, bumps in stock price move to a different drummer. Another fact *FORBES* doesn't want anyone knowing. List came out three months ago, stock was crickets-quiet until their Messiah guy died.

Only one way to find out what's going on is have a guy like you do what he does best, all right? Find nothing, no harm, no foul, we've got our noses clean, our ducks in order, a rising poohbah's gratitude. Never hurts, know what I mean?

His New Majesty's Baseline Report: Medical Staff Daily Log

Filed by: Nathan Bar-Ami, MD, PhD

Team: with the passing of His Late Majesty, our medical responsibilities have shifted to His New Majesty Hazoniyah, long may he reign. Switches are always complicated, hard to start treating someone who's suffered a clear shock and develop a sense of what is ordinary grieving and what is a worrisome condition. I took today's five minute check-in to see what I could glean, help us begin to consider a plan of action.

His New Majesty, to whom I will refer as HNMH for brevity, signed off on our seeing his past medical records, thank Gd, lets us see where we should hope/expect he'll return in the next couple of months. You may want to consult those records – I've attached them into the file we share – before reading on.

HNMH's vitals were a little off, perhaps to be expected in his circumstances, yet bears watching. Blood pressure, heart rate, temperature, perfectly understandable they'd be elevated in the first twenty-four hours after losing your father, the Messiah. I assume the letdown after the burial will take care of those.

His grief will bear more watching, I think, maybe because I have less experience with it. I know some will argue we should watch patiently, I'm not sure we as a nation have the time. Normal people might have the right to a month or six of slightly lower productivity as they recover from a blow, find their new normal without a loved one, kingship denies him that luxury.

When I saw him, he didn't say anything deeply disturbing, it's more of a sense of feeling bereft I think worth tracking. Sure, he's lost an historic figure and a father, sure, it has to be daunting to think you have to sit in his seat, you will inevitably be judged on how well you measure up to him. Still, he's been preparing for it, at some level, for twenty years.

I'd have hoped he'd be more ready.

As I said, no cause for concern, I only wanted to start the clock on our watchful waiting, be sure we see progress as events progress.

Please remember to update the log daily, whoever's on shift. Thanks.

Funeral Tickets Special Request Form

From: Reuven HaOzer, proprietor, The Temple Grounds.

To: Shin Bet Messiah Funeral detail, David Held, commander.

Re: Tickets for Employees.

Davidi, I need a solid, I'm having trouble staffing the shop for the funeral. My baristas want to be with the rest of the Jewish people showing the royal family how much His Late Majesty mattered. Obviously, I want to help them, except I need them here until the very last minute – you *know* I'm going to have customers right up to when the casket enters the courtyard, and probably a smattering throughout the funeral.

We both know some of those will need the full therapy service, will have decided there's no way the government would close *him* or *her* out for showing up a bit late, will be sure a bit of a fuss will get them in. With another bunch who expect the same, without the fuss part. Because if you're high up enough on the A list to secure a ticket without going through the lottery, you'll be sure you're too important to exclude, regardless of how often or somberly the government announces the rules, am I right?

You know your job better than I do, I only know here at the Grounds, our busiest time of day is fifteen minutes before and ten minutes after closing. Got bad enough I moved closing time ten minutes earlier. I'd bet you some pretty *shekel* you'll have dozens of people outside each entry point, waiting for the break after the first Psalm. Heck, you might have latecomers through the second or third eulogy.

Your problem, you'll handle it your way. My problem is baristas. They're thrilled my deal with the city and government grants tickets to all full-time staff, I've had a bunch of part-timers take me up on my offer to become full time. They all want to be seated punctually, would hate to be part of a scene where they're asked to be quiet or find their seats. I guess when you work where customer service means dealing with all sorts of annoying people, you're dead-set on not becoming like them.

I know how hard a time this must be for you, how many "friends" are popping up to make this exact kind of request. And I know I'm being a little hypocritical, making fun of other people's sense of how much they matter, then asking for an exception, as if I matter more. My only excuse is how much this matters to the *store;* going to bat for staff is part of how I retain them, avoid their opening competitive stores and dilute the quality of our product.

It's a limited resource, good baristas also adept at listening. Too many locations, we'll have too few qualified people, the disaster stories of bad or inattentive advice will start, whole industry might collapse.

You know the government agrees, you've seen the awards and certificates they've given us, and these are the people crucial to our success. I'm asking for a touch of help, maybe a door they can slip through after the proceedings have officially started, seats they can sneak to while everyone's standing to watch the royal family enter.

One more favor. I know it's chutzpah, and I am embarrassed, my only defense is the staff cares, and therefore it affects the people we help, etc. I need one or two to stay with me through the reading of the Psalm, in case we underestimated how many customers we'd have.

I'm not complaining, it will be a great day for business, much as we all sadly accept the Divine decree to take Our Late Majesty away from us sooner than we would have wished. I'm conceding my limitations, I won't be able to cover it all myself. You don't want a riot up by my place to add to your troubles, do you? People are going to be in a bad mood, if service falls short, not good, you know?

Oh, and on the topic, I'm worried about post-funeral, you know how hungry and anxious death makes people, they'll be swarming for comfort food. Is there a way I can sneak four or five baristas back before anyone else leaves? I guess my idea would be to escort them out, somehow, as the royal family and pallbearers assemble for the trek to the cemetery. Do you have a way?

So, three requests, three solids I'll owe you. Yes?

RESPONSE: DENIED

To: Reuven HaOzer, Proprietor, Temple Grounds

FROM: David Held, Cmdr, Shin Bet, Messiah Funeral Detail

Proprietor HaOzer, this office has considered your requests regarding the funeral for His Late Majesty, Sar Shalom, Light of Our Eyes, Redeemer of All Israel. Shin Bet regrets to inform you we are unable to accommodate you. Former Chief of Staff Shani Feinbaum did intervene as you asked, did convey the Palace's positive disposition to your contributions to society's health.

We assure you it was unnecessary, Shin Bet always cooperates with Jerusalem businesses to the maximum possible. We cannot explain further, Shin Bet does not comment on issues of protection and security. We can say we do always stretch to minimize the disruptions created by Palace security needs.

Unfortunately, the international attention to these events forces us to adopt a more formal and rules-based approach than usual. The Foreign Ministry has cautioned us, several times, about being sure outsiders don't come away thinking we give preferential treatment to our own.

Someone catches your people getting special treatment, posts it, some VIP is made to wait for ten minutes, if it's the wrong one, a bigwig from outside the country, even a Jewish one, has paid through the nose, she'll scream bloody murder to whoever will listen. Then, the news will snag an interview with some security guy from Vanuatu or wherever, who'll be happy to stick it to us, talk about the rigors of professionalism, no exceptions, no special favors, no *protekzia*, she or he will intone, somberly, as if they've never had lapses. Black eye's not worth it, believe me. For *this* funeral, we're by the book. Completely.

We attach the passes you requested, remind you attendees are urged to leave ample time for security and to be seated a full half-hour before the start of the ceremony. We wish you and all the Jewish people the fullest comfort at this hard time. May we all soon see the Resurrection, be reunited with our lost loved ones, and His Late Majesty.

(Editor: The rest of this was a handwritten scrawl below the official stamp and signature; I may have missed some words, this is what I could decipher. Sorry for the intrusion, dropping into the background again.)

Hey, man, really sorry, they're cracking down like crazy, told us a zillion times any hint of favoritism will bring the "direst of consequences," their words. Rumor is the Palace (read: His New Majesty, long may he reign) worries any glitches will raise questions about his handle, will land him behind the eight ball in public opinion.

Best I could do, I did, I picked your people's seats myself, great visibility, literally at the exits, with permission to leave before the Levi sings, if you or they want. If they complain about missing the *Kel Malei* – and I see why they would, Head Levi Amram's voice is unbelievable, imagine you have to tell your friends, no, I didn't stay, had to run back to serve people wrapped up in their own problems on a day like this – I can tell you he's decided to solo the Psalm of the Day each morning and afternoon this week, to honor His Late Majesty's memory. It'll be quieter in the store those days, you can offer to let them out to catch it.

Anyway, if they use the seats, jump out before the *Malei,* they should be back to help you, time to spare. Sorry I can't do better, beers on me next time. Cold comfort, I know, all any of us can do right now.

A Protocol Question

From: Palace Head of Security

To: Our Most Honored *Nasi,* R. Yohanan Attarah, Shani Feinbaum on behalf of the Royal Family, and Our Most Esteemed High Priest, Pinhas

Re: His New Majesty's Participation in the Funeral Procession

Our Honored Master and Teacher,

His Honor Rabbi Attarah did me the great favor of taking a moment to explain the limitations on His New Majesty's participation in tomorrow's events. I took careful notes, and it seems to me His Honor very clearly ruled His New Majesty would have to proceed directly from the courtyard of the Kotel back to the Palace, to wait there for the return of the rest of the family from the funeral procession, the eating of the meal of comfort, and beginning of the mourning.

I shared my understanding with His New Majesty (with your permission, and only for the sake of brevity, meaning no disregard, I will henceforth refer to him as HNM), who was, I say delicately, displeased. My awe of HNM and the throne he occupies obligated I bear his words in silence, and I did, especially as I am no scholar or legist.

I turn to the three of you for assistance and advice as to how to move forward. Should I plan to assign a detail to go with HNM from the courtyard to the Mount of Olives? Will HNM be returning directly to the Palace?

I apologize in advance for burdening your honored and busy selves with this matter at this busy time. It did seem urgent to me, and I hope I have not miscalculated. With great thanks,

NAME REDACTED

Joint Reply

To: NAME REDACTED, Palace Head of Security

From: R. Yohanan, High Priest Pinhas, Shani

Thanks for writing; indeed a tough time for us all, HNM (nice acronym, well done!) included. We have arranged to meet with him, in the presence of his dear mother, may the Lord grant her long and healthy years, and we believe it will be taken care of. Plan for HNM to remain in the Kotel courtyard until the procession leaves. We will make clear to all attendees they can either join the procession, as they should, or stay in their seats until after HNM also leaves, in the opposite direction, after the procession is gone.

We promise you, by the time we leave HNM tonight, we'll all be clear about the procedure. We'll update you if anything changes. With great appreciation for all your hard work,

R. Yohanan Attarah, Head of Sanhedrin,
High Priest Pinhas,
and Shani Feinbaum, His Late Majesty's Aide

Phone Records, ABC News/ Entertainment, Call 743 of April 8, 2048

(Voice-activated transcription, checked for accuracy by Ryan Williamson III's staff, re-checked by court's clerks as Plaintiff's Exhibit P-43201 in the wrongful termination lawsuit)

Hi, Janet, it's Ryan. I'm sorry, Nancy, oh, you prefer I call you Ms. Gulderson, my apologies, I didn't realize Shirley hired a new Admin. This is Ryan Williamson, the Third, if it's full names we're giving, calling for Shirley Beattie, please. Yes, she knows who I am, Ms. Gulderson. Listen, honey, you sound very sweet, I bet we could enjoy a lovely dinner together sometime, and I bet you think you're standing up for yourself right now by asking me not to be too familiar with you.

Your mistake, Ms. Gulderson, making me speak formally to you won't do a bit to stop me from inviting you to a hotel or somewhere, sweetheart. Best way to fend off unwanted advances in *your* job is to do topflight work, make yourself someone a person like me will be too afraid to rock the boat. One way you could do your job better? Memorize the *voices* of Shirley's bosses, let alone names. I'm the Sr. Exec Veep for News here at ABC, Shirley and I have a 7:30 meeting practically every night.

Oh, you leave at five? Another mistake – if you want to get ahead without providing extracurricular favors to guys like me, be indispensable to *her,* stay until she does or kicks you out, check her calendar, give her a brief rundown of her night, wait for her to say, "thanks, Nancy" you do let *her* call you Nancy, don't you? *Then* go. She doesn't care? Some shipshape crew she's running.

No, Missy, it's not all right, leave aside my voice or name, I can't imagine Shirley wants you grilling random callers. Some producer she's been recruiting, you think she wants you asking who this is and what they want from

Shirley? Try: 'Will she know what this is about?' Or, ask Ms. Beattie for better instructions. Yes, thanks. Talk again? I doubt it.

Shirley, Ryan. YANK HER NOW! Good idea, yanking the girl would be great, too, she just cost me time I don't have. But I meant Tucker, and yes, RIGHT NOW! Slip in a rerun of some ever popular thing, I don't care what. Ratings are dropping like a stone, this is such a disaster, I'm shaking, I can't tell you how many of us are about to lose our jobs, maybe careers, unless we turn in one of the greatest salvage operations in history.

I'm hanging up, call me back when it's done. Take her off, apologize to viewers, recommend CNN, maybe we can earn a few cooperation points. Call me back, soon as it's done. Yes, I know I said that, I want to be sure you call me back as soon as it's done. Then hang up and get on it or I'll say again call me ba – Took her long enough.

Maggie! Call the production guy at CNN, what's his name, right, it's a woman, the pert brunette, Alison something, right, tell her we're about to link our feed to theirs, they should please start tracking for the agreed fees. No, we'll trust them, long as she can't say she never knew to start counting. Maybe this Tucker fiasco won't be a complete loss, I guess, but pretty close. Leanne will have my head, is that a metaphor for anything other than firing me?

Ryan Williamson III! Yeah, hi, Shirley, thanks for calling back and handling it promptly. Why did I say she had to come off? Are you serious right now? We must not have been watching the same broadcast or we're in very different professions. Let's start with some positive, those are the new rules, right, show the positive or be suspect of prejudice, can't have that, right?

I will say, she looks better than I expected from when she wanders the halls here, good to know she can still clean up, v important to our viewers. Still has her sparkle, too, *I* wanted to watch her and I don't even like her. Stuff we could work work with, perhaps, although we do need to find a way to impress upon her how important it is for the weight to come off, you know? Ach, don't give me crap about it, sure, I have my own handles, we're not in a fight for people to watch me, you know? Leave that aside, maybe we'll find a way to make her too busy to overeat. More important you help her steer clear of the rookie mistakes, I would have thought a reporter of her experience would know to avoid, especially one who's spent the past ten years giving exactly these kinds of notes to younger anchors and reporters, for crying out loud.

What do you mean, I'm being too harsh? I'm supposed to believe she forgot viewers have no idea how a Jewish funeral works, they need her to tell them, step by step, without being made to feel stupid? I don't care if they think they want to be shown, not told. You think people who tune in to a funeral in a foreign language aren't hoping for a little telling? You think they don't know they'll miss cultural references otherwise, will cut her a little slack to explain without finding the trick to pass it off as if she's just showing it to them?

Sure, they want her to camouflage it as part of the translation, but they want her doing it. And if she overdoes it, everyone knows where the mute button is. Besides, if she's so worried, what was she doing giving the whole story of how he became king? This is his *funeral,* one or more of the *eulogies* gives his life story, the people she's talking to made the decision to tune in, they *know* he's important, she should have been telling them other stuff.

More granular? Fine: Why exactly did my screen not have an English translation of the Psalm the rabbi was reading? Why is all I know about these speakers a name and title? Is Rachel Tucker assuming we're all as up on the players as she is? She's not up on the players? Then why is she not sharing the info I know she gathered for herself, to follow what was happening?

Have you checked EuroNews or United Africa? You watch *those* channels, you know as much as a native Israeli, what's that word they use? Yeah, *sabra,* that's it, the kind of thing I'm talking about. Did she think our viewers enjoy being pelted with opaque terms, like Sanhedrin? Yeah, I looked it up, do you think our viewers want to have to ask their Amazecho a word every two seconds? Actually, it is my concern, Shirley, it's my *job* to care about these kinds of things!

Or how about: why didn't she find an expert to come on air for a thirty second mini-lesson on how their courts combine the judiciary with the legislative? I know she's a pretty face, viewers still want variety, might have drawn people in, not left them feeling as lost as back in high school.

Oh, you checked, and the ratings were fine? Why, because CNN and Fox were only ticks ahead of us? Shirley, we usually wipe their butts in this slot. This is the event of the century, we're *down* viewers from a reality show, how crazy is that? It's not a public service if no one's interested, Shirley.

Enough, you've made your point, you're loyal to underlings, good for you. I have three meetings piling up while we're arguing, time for me to tell you what has to happen, because if you make me show you, it will happen to you, too. You need to *tell* her she better pick up her game, too clearly to leave room for misunderstanding. Yes, implied or threatened outright.

We lost the funeral, there's no getting it back. She has maybe the week – what do they call it where they sit around and mourn? Perfect, she has until the end of the *shiva* to grow an audience; because if she can't draw viewers, Legal tells me we have a defensible claim she's in breach of that albatross of a contract the idiot two before me in this chair signed with her. Crazy what some people will do to bring a smile to a pretty face, time for us to dig out from under. Or for her to earn her keep.

Sure, she could win a lawsuit, it'd be *years* down the road, our lawyers are masters at making sure pre-trial, trial, appeal drag on until the money we ended up paying her would be worth a fraction of what it is now. And we both know she needs it now. I'm not worried, is my point. She finds a way to add value, glad to keep her. We need the value added, soon. Or it's firing and whatever comes.

Get on it, and report back. Sorry if my adamant came off as harsh or rough, I don't have the luxury of pussyfooting, there are jobs on the line, you know? Ok, thank you.

Evening Debrief, Funeral Day, 25-26 Nisan, 5808, 24th Year Since, Etc.

Staff Member at Closing: Reuven

Hey gang, here's the catch-up for the early shift, I'll be in around ten, funeral recovery made it a late closing. We had the uptick in business an hour and a half before the funeral, nothing worth a long review, mostly people with grief and anxiety, we were fine.

Crowd cleared out like a fire drill an hour later, seems the warnings worked, no one wanted to find out *this* was the time the doors really did close ten minutes before official start time. On the courtyard, in an apartment with unobstructed views, with friends watching screens in the comfort of their home, wherever people went to see the events, they were more careful about getting there with plenty of time than I've ever seen.

Weren't empty threats, either, give credit to the security guys, they followed through. I saw a billionaire – you would all recognize his name – race past the shop with eight minutes until start, was sure they'd bend the rules, hustle him to his seat after a quick check. Must have been tempting, too, if there's only one or two latecomers, you figure, who does it hurt?

He was back ten minutes later, buying muffins for the apology he owed the security guards in whose direction I hear he threw an epic tantrum. Beware little guys with power, he said to us. I suggested he'd best drop the thought, the security people would pick up on the attitude no matter how deep he thought he'd buried it, part of their job. It worked, he came back later to buy *me* a muffin. Which, yes, I know I don't need, thanks for your good wishes.

We did have a little crowd, missed first entry, came to us with help relaxing before the line formed for late entry. Upbeat bunch, surprising when you remember they'll have to admit to friends and family they could not get organized enough to take full advantage of scoring a ticket to the funeral of the century!

Always time for coffee, they said. Besides, who are we to complain, imagine the mourners!

Our attention-needy regulars were, of course, in their seats a full hour before start, came our way only after it was all done. They would have soaked up all the energy in the room except by then Limor, Jared, Evan, and Fiona had made it back, kudos and thanks to them for speed and alacrity. Shout out to Shin Bet for the seats with quickest access back to the store; Davidi Held will be in in the next few days, be sure to thank him and his officers for their service.

Kudos also to the rest of today's group, back on duty a half hour after the procession left the courtyard. Not easy, weaving your way through those crowds.

Some post-funeral rush, am I right? Bigger (and yes, more profitable per person) than I expected, you all did a bang-up job, I hit my quota for the month, I love the flexibility to rove, greet, triage, visit other branches. Today, I took the door on the way out, people were sated emotionally as well as physically. Good on you, or well done, you, as you guys like to say.

I've attached the supplies report, placed the orders shown; if you think we're running out of something, please do check my list before adding it to the Needs Doc, thx.

A piece of sad news, minor in context, a casualty of the day. You know the glass coffee pot from my mother's house, the one I used to refill people too focused on conversation to place another order? She's gone. No big drama, someone I knew a long time ago, was sure I'd never see again, walked into the store, as if she did it every day. Pot just slipped out of my hand, made a nice loud embarrassing crash as it shattered. Thanks to Javier for the quick clean-up.

I know you all want details, want me to lay out the scene, describe the furniture and the atmosphere and every tick of my emotional clock for the five seconds it took. Trust me, it's nothing. Her name's Rachel Tucker, she's on assignment for ABC, came into the shop in a professional – I repeat, yentas, professional, *not personal* – capacity, work issues she wanted advice on, summarized in the attached files. Confidential, remember.

I'm sharing it at all because if she comes in again, it's important you know to treat her no better or worse than any other customer, she'll be annoyed if staff brings up her celebrity. You don't have to play dumb, feel free to call her Ms. Tucker right away or whatnot. Nothing more, no autographs, no sly hints, no matter how innocuous you think a little teasing is, we clear?

Also, to explain the missing pot and to ask you to direct her my way. Pull her file only if Gd decides to take me from the store for a long time, you all know the drill. Other than that, I think she prefers speaking with me for now.

Short version, her job's at risk, the suits – they call them khakis these days, no one in New York wears a suit anymore – pulled her off the air in the middle of the funeral, put an official warning in her file, the first step to terminating her contract, she told me. Didn't make sense to me, I watched a few minutes of her coverage, ABC would never have left it on the Web if she was that bad. There's more going on there, I think.

And she was most definitely not that bad. Look, I've absorbed our Israeli ability to quibble, ABC's viewers are mostly Americans, I caught nothing they would have noticed.

I did ask some questions, you all know me, like why she hadn't refused to yield the mic, insisted on finishing the broadcast. Or, if on-air drama automatically puts her in the wrong, why she didn't file a grievance. I'm sharing her answer in case we meet up with other Americans in the same situation, allows us to understand better the pressures weighing on them.

College tuition, can you imagine? She said, it's a perk of the job, stops if they fire her, can take years to win a lawsuit, colleges won't let the kid finish while the case winds it way through the system. I couldn't believe it, looked it up, here's the link, only the top tenth of a percent afford it on their own, the rest need the discounted rates big corporations can force. Top reason Americans hang on to jobs they hate, according to the best surveys.

One of those moments, you realize you used to be close to someone, you started in the same place, took your first steps on different roads, ended up miles apart. You can't go home again and all that.

I repeat, this is all only for deep background, in case I'm out and she ever comes in again. I doubt it'll happen, for reasons I've included in the confidential file, I'm following protocol because if I don't, who will? I'll update you, as per procedure, if she comes back. And no betting pools, please, it's annoying enough when I am in fact going out on a date, let alone here.

Finally, for those of you who did me the favor of missing Princess Jo's eulogy to help with the rush, I contacted the palace, they gave me an unofficial transcript, and I've attached it.

Have a great night, see you guys in the morning.

The Eulogy of Princess Yeho'adan For Her Father, His Late Majesty, Light of All Israel, Sar Shalom, Unofficial Version

At the end of the prophet Elijah's life, his student Elisha sees him ascend to heaven in a fiery chariot. Elisha tears his clothing, and says, "*Avi, Avi, rekhev Yisrael u-farashav,* my father, my father, the chariot of Israel and its horsemen." We Jews have always since bid farewell to our greatest figures with those words, chariots and horsemen, who lead us through and into history.

I learned the verse in sixth grade, and it says perhaps too much about me when I tell you I was thinking then how well the verse fit the final farewell I would one day bid my father. I was a precocious eleven, gloomy verging on morbid, raised to think long term as well as short. Father, as I was allowed to speak of him in public back then, had won his third term as Prime Minister, the eleven year old me could sense he was by far not done.

It was how people treated him, already back then. His first two terms, his work affected my life mostly when people approached us on family outings, at restaurants, parks, the odd museum. He felt obligated to give them a minute or two, take a picture, sign a piece of clothing or other memorabilia. Those who wanted more time, he'd direct them, politely but firmly, to contact his office for an appointment. He always apologized to us afterwards.

The third term, the boundaries on his private life started to loosen. He was the people's leader, he felt, owed them more than a photo op, somewhere in my self-absorbed sixth grade mind, I understood and agreed, the adjustment from a father who's a politician to a father who's the Leader of All Israel. It was almost worse than when he and everyone finally gave in, saw he was Messiah, because the pomp and circumstance of the monarchy created enough distance for us to find a private him again.

The pairing of the election with learning the verse in school made me worry all I'd have of him would be a chariot and horseman, worry I'd lost the man who had pushed me on the swings for hours. For a girl starting the trek into womanhood, lack of a steady or meaningful father figure, the feeling of being tossed aside for politics, it could have been a disaster.

He saved it, the man you all know as His Late Majesty, Light of our Eyes, managed to continue to find time to be *Avi, Avi, my* father, the father I had always known, even as he became king, the anointed one of Israel, even as I had to begin curtsying when I entered his presence in public. Not as much time as before or as I would have liked, but time.

The previous speakers here today shared some excellent stories, and I thank them, for myself and at the request of my mother, my brother, Our New Majesty Hazoniyah, my other siblings, nieces and nephews. All my predecessors at this podium spoke eloquently and movingly, admirably fulfilled the first rule of a eulogy, bring the person to life, help everyone see a side of him we had not known before. I leave this funeral with the dear gift of a richer sense of my father, and hope over the course of *shiva* and beyond to hear more such stories – or to read them, with thanks in advance to all who honor us by submitting them to the website – the kinds of tidbits his family doesn't always know, much as we had the good fortune to spend hours with him each day.

I am leaving my own stories for the family *shiva*. I apologize, they are too personal for public consumption. I only want you to know there *are* such stories.

My family and I today join you in mourning our king, to me a mentor as well as father, who made me earn every role I filled, made me show I had developed the requisite skills before I could take the next step up the ladder of the palace bureaucracy, who helped me grow by denying me any shortcuts because of the accident of my birth.

I am here to tell you my siblings and I mourn that man, as do all of you, while we also mourn our father, my mother mourns the man she met as Samson, my nieces and nephews mourn their *sabba*, their grandfather, and on and on in the widening circles of family and friends.

My father was Our Late Majesty and my Abba. I was happy to share Our

Late Majesty with all of you, I keep my Abba within my family and friends. He was *Avi, Avi rechev Yisrael u farashav,* my and our father, my and our leader. To this grateful daughter, his ability to be both, fully, may be more impressive than his rebuilding the Temple.

Thank you, Abba, and thank you all of you, those here now, those who came to watch his train go by these emotional past two days, those who will be with us on the procession to the cemetery, those who will join us during the *shiva,* those who participate virtually. Thank you. May his soul be bound up in the bond of life.

Grieving Palace Announcement 47

Starting tomorrow, daily through the end of shiva, the palace will open at nine AM for public condolence calls, last group to enter at four PM. The palace reminds the public, with apologies, to budget for long lines, with old-style screening. Anyone who arrives at the line before noon and does not make it in that day will have first priority for the next day.

Phone Transcripts, Royal *Shiva*, Day 2 (with thanks to Yoram Lassiter for permission to excerpt, *Our Late Majesty, Bidding Farewell*)

Ma'am? ---- here [name redacted], I'm stationed outside the palace, there's a woman. Yes, I know women are allowed, ma'am, the line's split about fifty-fifty. It's…she's talking to people on the line. Yes, ma'am, I understand talking's permitted, there's quite a din out here. It's, she has a video recorder. Yes, ma'am I know handhelds and selfies are also fine, I have memorized the rules, as instructed. It's, she's using a separate camera, like broadcast people.

Hold on, I'll ask. Rachel Tucker, she says, has a press pass, ABC News/ Entertainment. No, ma'am, no one on line has complained, it's, well, I wondered whether we want the world to see us making a couple of thousand people wait hours and hours to offer condolences. Should we worry about a black eye for inefficiency?

Yes, ma'am, I do know world leaders have lain in state with larger crowds and longer lines, I thought I should check, I've never been in a situation like this before. Yes, ma'am, none of us have, I agree.

No, she seems to have chosen one family. I saw her filming with all sorts of people before, maybe thirty seconds each. I don't know why, should I ask? Teasers? Could be, ma'am, excellent suggestion. Right now, she's in a longer interview with this striking couple, he's a Joe California type, four inches taller than me, neck says he's jacked. No, he's wearing a loose, long-sleeved shirt, I can't see. No sign of a belly, I don't know if it's a six or eight, but it's a pack.

You'd think, right? Nope, he went the other way, she's dark, real dark, Sefardi or mixed-heritage Ethiopian. I suppose she could be some other kind of African, they might have met in LA or something. Why do I say LA? She's American, I hear her English, he's gotta be from Cali, it's basically the only place I know where they put in the hours to look like that and also have rabbis whose conversions our government accepts.

I *am* from there, good memory, ma'am, thank you, my family came just about twenty-three years ago. Our family takes pride in my parents' being early adopters, spotting His Late Majesty for what he was. I was a kid. And as I recall, I shed more than a few tears, gave them more than a run for their money in my teens. Oh yes, ma'am, sorry, back to this family.

Age? They're parents, three kids, means what, mid-30s? Kids are, I don't know how old, I don't have any. I should guess? Ok, ballpark, ten, seven, five? No, she's filming all of them, kids popping in every minute or so, mom's shushing them sometimes, other times not, pride in her eyes, I guess Tucker's directing some questions at them. Sorry, ma'am, Ms. Tucker.

They're in pen 7, give me a second to do the math, pens move every fifteen minutes as the fifty in the palace finish. We started intake at eight, puts them twelve pens back, I guess, means they showed up around 7:30. I don't know where they're from, Ma'am, you told us not to badge by geographic region.

Not a complaint, no, ma'am, an explanation for the paucity of facts. I called without much to say because I worried you wouldn't want this broadcast in real time or perhaps for the duration of the *shiva,* or perhaps at all, and I know anything recorded, free speech types will say we have to let them show it.

Do you want me to ask where they live? Yes, Ma'am, I know, I promise I can be tactful, polite, and respectful, I believe you told me you trusted me to run the detail because of my abilities to handle crowds, visitors, and short tempers.

Interrupt, or wait for a break? Yes, Ma'am, I am watching as we speak, they are caught up in what they're doing. Ok, I'll take a quick sweep, send you the pictures. I'll hold or you can call me back. All right, speak to you soon, thank you.

[Editor's Note: The security man seems to have forgotten to turn off the recorder after the call]. Ladies and gentlemen, we appreciate your patience, a small request: Please stay away from the walls of your pen, we've made them with lots of room to hold the fifty in your group, we don't want the walls falling, fights about who was in which group, pushing, shoving, any of that. With Gd's help and a little good will from us all, you'll all get in, and we thank you for the honor you show Our Late Majesty with your cooperation. Yes, sir, thank you, we did realize the crowds might grow as the week progresses, you're all fortunate, as of tomorrow we will have an hourly lottery for the right to join the line.

Excuse me, I have to answer this, I'm on call. [Redacted name]. Yes, ma'am, Ms. Tucker is still speaking with them. Ok, will do. Shani Feinbaum's authorization, excellent, it will help if other reporters wonder why Ms. Tucker's receiving special care, or if the food and drink vendors want to know why they have to keep their 50 yards of distance and she doesn't.

Yes, ma'am, you too, may we all find full and speedy comfort.

Rachel Tucker's Intake Briefing For *Shiva* Visit

Transcribed by: ABC News Intern [No name included]

STAMPED FOR INTERNAL USE ONLY [Editor's Note: Permission to reprint secured from ABC News, confirmation number 5923841, with my gratitude – GR]

Hi, Rachel, welcome to the outer courtyard of the Palace, I'm Shani Feinbaum, I was Chief of Staff for His Late Majesty, I'm coordinating the *shiva* for the royal family, part of being transition director, and, of course, Reuven and I go way back. He hasn't said anything about me? No, I suppose he wouldn't, he's pretty close-mouthed about that kind of stuff. I hadn't heard he knew you until the last couple of days, either.

Not my business right now, he can handle his past relationships however he decides. I meant me, actually, I have no idea if the two of you had enough of a thing to be called a relationship, and strong and silent here clearly has no interest in clearing it up. The two of us dated a bit, then for a long while were each other's safety spouses, you know, the person you keep on tap to marry if you're both still single by age whatever.

Oh, I'm sorry, both of you, I didn't mean to imply …no, no, no, Rachel, I promise, Reuven and I realized long ago we weren't going to be able to pull the trigger, bite the bullet, put your favorite idiom here. We turned thirty, our first deadline, Reuven begged off, I forget his gentle let down, I think he said something about advances in fertility medicine meaning we didn't need to rush, we agreed to wait until thirty-two. By then, I felt enough breathing room to suggest we wait another two years.

Eventually, we realized we would never both think it was right at the same time, the dance was putting a damper on our friendship, creating the real risk of losing each other. It was mutual, I promise, and years ago, no hard feelings on either side. Really, no hard feelings, not like where one side says it and the other's secretly gnashing his teeth. Really, no need to feel weird around me, I am not invested in Reuven in that way, not whatsoever.

Of course, sure, if you say there's nothing between the two of you, great, I believe. It's just, well, I was part of the team looked at your visa waiver. A formality, you could have probably come back here years ago, although ABC's making the request did bring it to the attention of G-14s like me; without, it might have gone to some frustrated G-5 who decided to have fun by making an example of you, keep you out forever for one bad mistake.

I seem to keep putting my foot further down my throat. I was *not* implying you should have been back here years ago, nor was I making any comment about how you raised your son, or whether you did or did not deny him a connection to his father's adopted homeland. And of course Reuven could have come to you had he wanted to, no one knows his hesitations about pursuing relationships better than me. I was only saying, I know some of your past, some of where you seemed to be heading back then. The report does make clear how close a call it was for you, the examiner expressed shock at your choice, thought for sure you'd choose Israel and life with Reuven.

Of course, of course, you say it's ancient history, I believe you. I only want to be clear, he and I are *really* ancient history, no torch, no wistfulness, no daydreams about ways the good Lord could bring us back together. You two revisit old times, great; you don't, great. Either way, nice to meet you.

Learned from His Late Majesty not to make business contacts personal? Hah, hah, no. I learned almost everything from him, and His Late Majesty drilled into us the importance of making *everything* personal, especially politics.

Any time a decision would hurt some people, no matter how many more we'd help – every damn day in government, in other words, pardon my language – he would ask us to speak in favor of an idea only if we were willing to ask our mother, father, brother, sister, child, to make the sacrifice. And definitely make it ourselves, as he sometimes required us to do.

No brushoffs allowed, either. One time, I made the mistake of saying, "well, those guys deserve it," and he gave me the worst tongue lashing I ever received, or saw him administer.

'*They* don't think they deserve it! How are you going to convince *them* they deserve it? If you can't, are you ready for them to be waiting for the next opportunity to dish it back? Don't give me the Torah says no revenge, I know that as well as you. If even fifty percent of us acted the way the Torah said, a Messiah would have beaten me here a thousand years ago!"

A couple of times, he made a few of us live with the people whose lives we were about to hurt or make harder, told us to come back only when we could articulate exactly how they felt about it, exactly how they saw it, could see how they could think they were right. And he made us do it in front of the very people who had opened their homes to us, at his personal request.

That's a boss.

Please forgive me, yes, thank you for the tissue. As I talk about him, I remember him, and when you've had one mentor your entire adult life, who managed to be both the Messiah and the most down to earth boss you could hope to have, the pain doesn't go away on a dime.

Ok, enough about me, sorry for rambling, His New Majesty asked me to be sure you feel the full warmth of the palace's welcome. Let's square the two of you away, we have seven minutes to ready you to join your group. They've gone through the scanners into the inner courtyard, let's catch up. Empty your pockets please, everything other than clothing, like I'm doing. Yep, even professional staff, each time in or out. Rachel, your equipment on the conveyor belt staffed by Adi over there, Reuven, where Zev is, thank you.

All set? All right, all the items you put on the belt, don't start replacing them, they're not going to see the palace, just you. Take one of those bags and markers, write your name and number, take good care of your claim check, we didn't bother computerizing this part of the process. Ok, ready? Dump it on the longer conveyor belt, it'll be waiting on your way out.

Sorry, no, nothing but the literal clothes on your back. Squared away? Great, let's join the group so you don't have to hear my spiel twice. Well, I'm here anyway, I figured I'd lead the group, best way to be around if you have questions as the visit unfolds.

Malachi, thank you, let me take this group, you take the next. Ladies and gentlemen, my name is Shani Feinbaum, I had the privilege of working for His Late Majesty from before he took the throne; on behalf of the royal family, I thank you for taking the time to join in their sorrow. They will tell you again themselves, have asked all palace staff to say it often. Living in the public eye makes the public – all of you – family, too. When bereavement comes, as it does to us all, the presence of family, nuclear and extended, comforts.

At the same time, life in the public eye means *shiva* cannot be as free-flowing as we all might have liked. Sadly, we couldn't be one hundred percent positive none of you would try to record or broadcast this private time, why we had to ask you to bag and check all possessions.

We *have* had some complaints, especially from foreigners, you're right, sir, they want pictures, don't know if they'll ever be back here, don't want any blank spaces in the record of the trip they'll force the gang back home to watch. Sadly for them, at times like these, the needs of the few mourners outweigh the needs of the many albums longing to be filled.

The royal family well understands virtually all of you have only the best intentions, would never break or bend the rules, are here to spend a few moments sharing our national grief. The royal family thanks you, the palace staff thanks you, and I thank you. Truly.

Still, for the possible one or two of all the thousands coming through here who thinks he or she will make a killing by bootlegging, we at the palace are forced to make clear we would take such an offense more seriously than you'd likely imagine. We're talking jail and a fine you *will* be paying off the rest of your life. No possibility of bankruptcy, clemency, or other foregoing of the full amount.

For those of you from elsewhere, there's more. I hope you understand the generosity in the royal family setting aside slots for foreigners, slots deducted from the citizens' lottery. I hope and believe none of you would abuse the privilege. In case you would, I remind you His Late Majesty used the leases of our security bubbles to extend the reach of Israeli security forces. Anyone here from St. Kitts and Nevis? Vanuatu? Kiribati? Switzerland? I didn't think so. Anywhere else, we have rock-solid extradition treaties, you should expect we will find you, and make it your problem we were forced to go to the trouble.

I apologize again for having wasted your time with a warning we at the palace are fairly sure does not apply to any of you. Unpleasantries accomplished, let's start over. Welcome to the Royal Palace, and thank you for your kind wishes for the mourners.

We urge you to take this moment to remember the names: Her Majesty, the Queen Mother Tanchumit, she should be separated for a long and healthy life, His New Majesty Hazoniyah, Princess Yeho'adan or Jo, Prince Achituv, Princess Keren HaPuch, His Late Majesty's surviving brothers Jordan and Adam, and sisters Leilani and Evangeline. Some members of the extended family may be in at any particular time, right now I think we have two or three grandchildren on site, some nieces and nephews as well.

The family has asked us to also apologize for the fifteen-minute time limit. They would have wished to act as any of you would, to greet each of you, hear your stories about His Late Majesty, leave up to you how long you sat. With groups of fifty – and I was there when palace security begged them to make the groups larger, the visits shorter, to keep the line moving, open fewer doors for any kind of mischief or mayhem – we have to do what's possible.

In the room, here's how it will go. After you enter and sit, the family will wait thirty seconds, it will feel longer, you never realize how slowly time drags until you're sitting in a large room with many people and no one's speaking. They don't want the experience too chatty.

Then, a family member will thank you for coming, in his or her own way, and tell a story about His Late Majesty. It may be one they experienced, or heard during these *shiva* visits, to remind you your contribution matters, may be shared with other people down the line. They will ask if one of you has a story – anyone? Yes, ma'am, you? Just to check, are you sure you can tell it in less than five minutes?

Great. Then, Ms. – oh, sorry, Mrs. Dietcher will tell her story, the family spokesperson will ask anybody else for a brief thought, anyone? You, sir, yes, thank you. The group will sit for another few quiet moments, and then I will rise, you'll rise with me, we'll recite the ritual words of condolence, they're on the card you're being given now, which also has bullet points of everything I just said. And we'll exit.

Questions? No? Excellent. Well then, again, with thanks from the royal family and the request to stop all conversations from now until the other side of the palace, please follow me.

Whistleblower Report, ABC News, April 10, 2048

To: Vera Finley, Ombudsperson, ABC News/Entertainment

Cc: Buffy Dachs, Ombudsperson, Walt Disney Co., Chip Kelter, Ombudsperson, ABC

From: Shirley Beattie

Re: Ryan Williamson

Note: WHISTLEBLOWER PROTOCOL INVOKED!

Per Policy 7256, manual 42-Q, lodged at ABCNewsEntertainment.com/policypractices, and as advised by counsel, Lorraine Branson of Mitchells, Deere, and Drye, LLP, I, Shirley Beattie, submit this formal complaint regarding Ryan Williamson, my direct report.

As per company regs, I have discussed the testimony with my therapist, to be sure Mr. Williamson's frequent assertions of my oversensitivity are not relevant. I am prepared to reveal her identity, to sign a release allowing her to speak freely about our sessions regarding Mr. Williamson, should a court or arbitrator require it, although only to the court or arbitrator. Based on the advice of therapist and counsel, I am here to point out clearly illegal behavior of Mr. Williamson's, leaving aside the many ways he manages to stay just inside lines authorities would address, enjoin, or punish.

His clearly illegal act starts with his recent request/ order to terminate Rachel Tucker's Jerusalem assignment. As you may recall, it was he who insisted she return to on-air reporting, despite the many qualified staff who could have flown there from nearby countries, as usual in such cases. Against her wishes, he insisted she be on site at the funeral for the recently deceased King Sar Shalom, threatened to terminate her unless she agreed.

This alone was likely a violation of her contract, except he knew family issues precluded her litigating the matter to its just conclusion.

She went with the explicit time frame of the funeral, week of mourning following, and possibly more. I expected – to make clear these were not her pipe dreams, they were the team's understanding – she would have this time to find her sea legs before any executive decision or review on and of her performance.

Mr. Williamson has now asked me to terminate her *employment,* not just her assignment in Israel, because she failed to secure footage of her recent condolence call at the Palace. This alone, while not illegal, does flout company policy 35923, laid out in manual 22Y: "termination with prejudice shall be limited to employees who violate felonies, abuse substances, or show gross incompetence."

Considering the rules laid out by Israel's royal family, across many platforms, prohibiting recording devices of any sort, Mr. Williamson's complaint is clearly out of place. Nor did he bother to credit Ms. Tucker's initiative in securing entry to the palace at all. The lottery had precious few slots for foreign nationals, *zero* set aside for registered journalists, it's why no one else had any version of the story from any closer than the outer areas. *Her* connections cleared a path to the special consideration she received, a path we believe will continue to lead her to stories our viewers want to see and hear.

The reason he's giving for firing her, I contend, is more properly seen as a reason to applaud her, give her more time, not less.

(My personal friendship with Ms. Tucker allows me to share background I think makes her conduct more impressive. The "source" she cultivated for a chance into the palace for a condolence call is a former boyfriend, Reuven HaOzer, long story, bad breakup, part of the reason she left with no plans to go back, the visa issue our lawyers had to clear. Her willingness to turn to him on our behalf seems to *me* beyond the call of duty. Sticking to the palace's rules mattered to preserving the relationship. Right-thinking people would laud her choice.)

Mr. Williamson's termination order further chose to ignore ways she mitigated the lack of footage from inside the Palace. Showing up early for what was already a story no other reporter had, she scouted people on line, filmed brief interviews with them on the way in, a thirty-second post-mortem with them and with each of the members of her own group when they left, reactions still fresh and raw.

I could have turned those into five minutes of air time as good and interesting as the visit itself, had Mr. Williamson not thrown his fit and confiscated the file. These people telling us what they had just experienced brought it to life better than being shown it in real time, because they fleshed out what we might not have noticed.

My lack of prior complaints should show you I work to fly beneath any political radar in our company. It would have been much easier for me to obey, fire her, and protect myself. I couldn't do it when I knew a board of review would have found at most "should have done better," not open to termination, more likely would have come back with "shows commendable flexibility under pressure."

I am aware policy 2632, manual 58H, limits whistleblowing to a demonstrable pattern of conduct. For that reason, I share what some might like to dismiss as old news, Mr. Williamson's repeated derogatory comments about Ms. Tucker. I did document them as they occurred, as the time stamps show, and they are attached.

Until Mr. Williamson's arrival at ABC News/ Entertainment, Rachel's performance reviews were uniformly excellent, earning her the lucrative contract extension he resents for its constricting his budget – as he has said in my presence multiple times, I am not guessing or mind-reading.

Relevantly, none of his qualms made an appearance in his first three months heading our division. Then, as per attachment three, he asked Ms. Tucker to join him for dinner, violating company policy 0000128, manual 1A. When she declined, I was not the only one who noticed his extended funk (as per testimonies I took at the time, also attached).

Attachments seven through eleven document his focus on her contract thereafter, his newfound frustration with prior management's financial freewheeling largesse, at cost to his freedom to shape the division his way; his attempt, all the way to an appeals process, to void her contract for her refusal to undergo cosmetic surgery to extend her on-camera career. Attachment fourteen is his memo sending Ms. Tucker to report from the funeral, fifteen his memo to remove her during.

I hope you recognize the pattern here: the moment he realized nothing would happen between them personally or physically, he fixated on her cost, began a campaign to get rid of her, in the face of much evidence of her value, including the slew of younger anchors she has mentored, their glowing testimonials also attached.

Per regulation 631881AQF, subsection 3, requiring an **action recommendation**: Ms. Tucker should be reinstated quickly, called and reassured of her safety on the job before she files the lawsuit a judge will not allow her to drop until we satisfy said judge Rachel has received just compensation for her troubles; clear her file of Mr. Williamson's complaints; and discipline him. It is not my place to be more specific about his discipline, because a) my friendship with Ms. Tucker means I cannot possibly be dispassionate about what he deserves, and b) I do not know his other contributions to the company, for all I know significant ones. I have heard rumors of family connections and vital lines of credit.

Lest this be seen as a ploy or play for independence on my part, I am comfortable suggesting three of my colleagues to step into my current role, happy to take an equivalent job elsewhere in the division. Clearly, also, my anonymity must be protected, or I, too, need to be walled off from Mr. Williamson for the rest of his and my time with ABC.

Respectfully,
Shirley Beattie,
assisted by Lorraine Branson,
Mitchells, Deere, and Drye, LLP

Security Waiver for Reuven HaOzer/Rachel Tucker at Palace Senior Staff Meeting

From: Shani Feinbaum, Transition Director

To: Palace and Government Security and Privacy Service, David Held, Unit Commander

Re: Special Guests for Cabinet meeting, Tuesday, 2nd Day New Moon of Iyyar, April 14.

Commander Held,

Allow me to offer heartfelt congratulations on the smooth funeral and *shiva*. No embarrassing leaks, no complaints about intrusive questioning or harassing body checks. Well done, it's not easy to balance citizens' comfort with careful protection, I'm happy you found the way, happy you took full advantage of the career opportunity. I hope you find similar satisfaction and success in your new position.

The substance: I'm writing to ask if we can include Reuven HaOzer and Rachel Tucker in tomorrow's senior staff meeting. I know you'll ask: I *did* clear it with HNM and Princess Jo, I'm not asking you to go behind their backs. They both made a point of insisting I inform you the idea is mine, they are aware of my request, have no objection to it, but are not weighing in on the issue, the request is mine alone. In other words, evaluate it by the standard you would use for the personal request of a former Chief of Staff and current Transition Director, not the standard for favors solicited by members of the royal family or HNM Himself.

HNM, especially, wanted me to stress his ascent to the throne has not deluded him into thinking he knows your job, can weigh in intelligently on what poses a risk to the privacy and security of the proceedings. I only also point out you know Reuven, it's hard to imagine he poses any kind of threat, and Ms. Tucker's a public figure. Internal Security's files on them are too thin and flimsy to bother to attach, proving my point, they're no physical security risk. Ms. Tucker's one unfortunate run-in is too long ago to count against her.

We might more realistically worry about information leaks, a worry I believe we can avoid by bringing Ms. Tucker in closer. To me, this meeting can be an audition, for HNM to see what I see, agree to give her "favored journalist" status, feed her a scoop every few days. Other agencies will follow the palace's lead, she'll be a fountain of stories no one else has, the go-to Israel reporter.

The beauty of the plan lies in how it cushions us against criticism. News agencies look to find the corruption in power, it's a sacred professional duty to hate the exceptional, to find the two examples out of a thousand we do not meet standards no one else bothers to set.

We'll have Rachel Tucker, an elite and trusted reporter. She'll tell them when we get it right where others won't, and when we misstep, if we've developed a relationship, she'll see the error in all its nuance, including the ways we plan to set right whatever did go wrong. Better, she'll be able to tell us if the repair we're envisioning will accomplish its goal.

We won't need spin or half-truths, we'll have a real truth and someone to convince the world of its accuracy. With her around, smears won't find traction. Anyone who does want to drag us through the mud, like maybe some of the Palace staff HNM is likely to encourage to move on, they'll have to speak with her, and she'll be able to show them how bad they'll look.

That's worst-case. Some part of me bets the world will go back to ignoring us, leaving an audience only enough for one full-time reporter. We cultivate Ms. Tucker, she'll be the one, and we'll have a way to spread the stories that deserve spreading. And yes, there will be stories the entire world wants; trust me, I've known HNM a long time, he just needs a little time to figure out the way from under his father's shadow. Speaking of whom, I heard His Late Majesty speak about HNM in private, and he was confident his son would make remarkable moves, in his time and at his pace. We want to be sure we have the way to tell the world about it, our way.

She can also be our test market of one. She finds our news exciting, she'll excite her audience, it'll snowball. We don't excite her, she can tell us what we need to do differently.

For all these reasons, and more, the Office of Palace Transition advances this formal request for the presence of Reuven HaOzer and Rachel Tucker at tomorrow's meeting.

With kindest regards, best wishes to you and yours for comfort for our national loss,

Shani Feinbaum

P.S. Davidi, ok, I understand you needed a paper trail, and Tucker's the concern there; between us, I really hope you can see your way to letting this happen, for Reuven's sake. I know he's a beer buddy of yours, not sure how much you guys talk about emotional issues, or if you've had a chance to catch up lately, you've been busy.

Here's what I know: she matters a lot more to him than he's admitting. It's the only reason I can think of for why he didn't tell me about her all these years. Also, we were on the verge of dating for a *decade*, I know his tells. He's walking taller, he may be wearing his same casual clothes, he's ironing them a lot more carefully these days. And, honestly, I never knew he *could* open his eyes as wide as he does when he's around her.

There might be more, I didn't test him against a checklist or anything, people already think I'm carrying a torch. Which I'm not!!! It matters here, for our government's purposes.

And he matters to her, the five minutes I had with her made clear, it's part of why I'm sure she won't do anything to betray the favor he did by asking us to put her in the room. Check the footage from the courtyard of the palace at the *shiva* visit, I know *I* caught six or seven flirting moves, and I was barely with them. And she asks him for advice *all the time*, it's either sickening, sweet, or both.

Point is, on this one, trust me, the past isn't dead, it isn't even past, as they say Faulkner said. Help Rachel Tucker, you're helping Reuven. I think it's a win-win, I hope you do, too, would be great if they could be there.

Best, Shani

Preliminary Minutes, Special Joint Cabinet Meeting

Attendees' Eyes Only, For Comments and Proposed Changes

From Transcribed Audio (available to attendees on request) by: Tamara Nahat, Temporary Recording Secretary

In attendance: All members of His Late Majesty's Cabinet and Advisers Without Portfolio as well as His New Majesty's inner staff. Princess Jo arranged members of the two administrations in alternate seats, to avoid groupthink. Seated at the wall were Reuven HaOzer and Rachel Tucker, as per Shani Feinbaum's request, authorized by Cmmdr. Held.

Meeting Called to Order: 9:30am, April 14, 2048, 2nd Day of the New Moon of Iyyar, 5808, the month of the recreation of the State of Israel, twenty-third year since the coronation of His Late Majesty, the Messiah, the anointed one of all Israel, King Sar Shalom.

9:32: His New Majesty Hazoniyah (henceforth: HNM) thanked all present for their visits and assistance during the *shiva*. "We arose this morning with much gratitude, to Hashem [Editor's Note: the way Israelis refer to Gd, Whose Name they invoke in full only during prayers or other rituals] for giving us Our father, may Our actions atone for his repose, for as long as we had him.

"On behalf of Ourselves, Her Majesty Our mother, may the Lord grant her many happy and healthy years, and Our siblings and extended royal family, We wish to convey the comfort we all took in your presence and prayers. You and the nation eased the burden of our loss with how well you conveyed its impact on each of you. Thank you."

Murmured responses around the table included some tentative suggestions HNM take the rest of the day to recover. Immediately rejected, HNM reminding the group of his responsibilities to the nation. "Our father always taught Us the needs of the nation override any personal indulgences we in the royal family may wish to take. Delaying a return to life and service for a day would betray Our father's memory and example, may Our actions atone for his repose."

Before he turned to the first agenda item, HNM called attention to the presence of the two guests, not bothering to identify Reuven HaOzer, definitely known to anyone authorized to read these minutes, and Rachel Tucker of ABC New/Entertainment. HNM said (with a twinkle in his eye, he told me to write) Ms. Tucker was there to develop a record of the kingdom's early days.

HaOzer and Tzachalon Har-Tuv, His Late Majesty's Chief of Security, raised their hands. Har-Tuv, called first, apologized for the impertinence, felt his role as Chief of Security obligated him to question Ms. Tucker's security clearance. Shani Feinbaum passed around copies of the waiver signed by David Held. Har-Tuv objected to having been circumvented, HNM thanked him for his concern, expressed his comfort with Commander Held's decision, asked Princess Jo to take time after the meeting to clarify the security assignments, and called on Levi HaOzer.

He had used the honorific before, why HaOzer now asked whether HNM would do him the favor of using his first name. HNM resisted the familiarity, chided HaOzer for asking for a breach of proper respect. Reuven asked HNM for permission to speak freely, then asked HNM to consider how approachability had always been his only mode of service.

"I know and respect many Levites whose perch of superiority, aura of separateness and elevation, fosters their success in their duties, whose students follow them precisely because they recognize the gap between their knowledge and the Levi's. Such has not been my lot, likely because of the many deficiencies in my knowledge and character. I have no hope of fooling anyone into thinking I rise above them.

"All I have, the only contributions to our national health I have been able to make, rest on friendships where I am occasionally fortunate enough to offer an apt word at a felicitous time. Put a title on me, even one as common as Levi, people will decide I'm a little arrogant, too full of myself, and turn to others."

HNM thought for ten seconds, said, "Perhaps Reuven," he tilted his head and raised his eyebrows, to be sure HaOzer noticed him respecting his wishes, "Perhaps Reuven has given us the ideal first item for our agenda today. We have been considering the unwieldy use of His New Majesty as a form of address. We remember well how much Our father, We hope to provide atonement for his soul, resisted wordy, lengthy, and flowery salutations, yielded only where advisers made clear they could not in good conscience act without awe of the throne and its occupant, nor countenance it in others. Do any members of this august group have thoughts on plausible alternatives to roll out to the public?"

Five minutes of discussion and a vote ratified the view of His Late Majesty's Secretary of Public Relations, Keren Shuvovitz, the administration should refrain from hasty changes. Over the next twelve months, while the law requires him to append "We hope to provide atonement for his soul" each time he mentions his father's name, he will continue to be His New Majesty.

Outside his presence, and in writing, the group agreed people could be encouraged to use HNM. Over the course of the year, HNM and staff will research options, with the tentative plan to shift to calling His Late Majesty "King Sar Shalom, ob"m" and HNM, "His Majesty."

From title, HNM segued into image and identity, who he should strive to be to, for, and with his subjects. He opened for comments with the words, "We will succeed only to the extent We find a smooth working rapport with Our people, as we all stride towards the future."

[Recorder's note: I have omitted specific names from the ensuing back and forth; in ten years, the original notes will become public. Despite Princess Jo's attempts, the meeting quickly split between His Late Majesty's staff and HNM's, allowing me to refer to any speaker from His Late Majesty's staff as OC (Old Cabinet), NC, New Cabinet, for HNM's people, despite HNM's having made few formal appointments.]

Princess Jo served as mediator, having worked with both. OC urged a show of strength, lest HNM spend his reign in His Late Majesty's long shadow. Money quote from outgoing Minister of Absorption (identified here with permission, proud of the stand he took):

"The people must learn they now live in His New Majesty's world; otherwise, we risk a coterie of malcontents, caught up in fake nostalgia for a false memory of the world of His Late Majesty. People address new realities grudgingly, and only when forced."

The New Cabinet worried about the younger generation, who had been chafing under His Late Majesty's strictness, cowed only by the prestige of the Messiah. They suggested HNM focus his first years on building a connection, fostering and earning loyalty with encouragement, enticement, incentives, heavier on the positive reinforcement than His Late Majesty.

Money quote (attribution classified): "Give *to*, build credit *with*, them, reap the profits for all His New Majesty's years, may Hashem grant long, healthy, and successful ones."

As if by a shared signal, they stopped, although each person around the table is known to have the substance to say plenty. Princess Jo and HNM requested and urged them to continue, more than once, eventually commanded them to, limited only by the need to speak with respect.

Finally, one NC (last time I will make a point of it; attributed quotes are with permission, unattributed ones are where the person insisted on anonymity) said, "With all the love, affection, and admiration we had and have for His Late Majesty, we believe his prestige was wearing thin among certain segments of our populace. To our limited understanding, matters might have come to a distressing and distracting confrontation – for all we hesitate to say the word, maybe a full-on rebellion – had old age and illness not brought a loosening of grasp.

"With His Late Majesty's passing, people are watching carefully and nervously, alert for any hint HNM will take up His Late Majesty's flag exactly where he dropped it."

Money quote, from the CFO of Israel Force Fields Inc., expected Incoming Minister of Commerce: "As soon as HNM brings an invention as world-changing as His Late Majesty's force field; doubles our GDP again through the worldwide licenses of this new invention; finds a building project as world-altering as the Temple; advances the cause of Torah as fully as His Late Majesty when he restored the Sanhedrin, populated it with rabbis astute enough to take tiny steps in building a religious country; as soon as His New

Majesty checks those boxes, the people will be ready to bear what outsiders might see as excessive authoritarianism. Until then? With all due respect, I believe I speak for my colleagues in recommending honey, not the lash."

His New Majesty followed the interchanges wordlessly, nodding at phrasings he liked, sharp points, from both sides, giving no sense of his instincts. Finally, Princess Jo halted debate, summarized the positions, said they seemed to be at an impasse. All eyes turned to HNM.

He nodded gravely, paused to collect his thoughts. "Our father, We should be an atonement for his repose, would have known instantly how to handle the situation. As if the Word of Gd spoke from his throat, he would by now be working on how best to implement the plan. It again reminds all of us of the enormity of our loss, another way we (and We) cannot possibly replace him. We must solicit more advice and more advice, until the way opens before us; it is the only way We have ever made progress, from before We were called to attempt to follow him on the throne.

"For a long time, We solicited the advice from His Late Majesty, our confidence in his ideas exempting us from a wider search. With his passing, We must return to diligent counsel-seeking." Jaws dropped as he then turned to the couple sitting in hastily commandeered folding chairs. "Mr. HaOzer, Ms. Tucker, what would you add? Yes, yes, We agree, you were led to believe you are observers, yet here you are, with ideas We can hope will help. Will you help?"

A cacophony of protests, with countercalls of support. HNM let it crescendo and crash, rise and drop, for seven minutes, held up a hand, drawing immediate silence. HNM repeated his request to Reuven HaOzer, his studied ignoring of the debate leaving no room for protest.

Reuven shook his head, said he had no reason to think his ideas should carry any more weight – "nay, much less," he said – than those of anyone around the table. The value he could add would come only from sharing the impressions he had had of the people who had come through the branches of his shop in the past week, hardly a randomized or sufficient sample.

HNM smiled. "Exactly the kind of information to spark inspiration. Please continue."

"They're not thinking in the same terms as the honored people around this table. They're not talking about how strict or authoritative His New Majesty might be. They're grieving, on top of which they're scared, as we all are, because death brings change, and we all instinctively cower in the face of a cloudy future. Maybe worse, His Late Majesty has given us complete security for long enough to make this uncertainty unsettlingly new for many.

"I don't know which way that cuts – maybe a confident and strict monarch will reassure them of the hand at the helm, like a firm swaddling for a newborn, a familiar similarity to His Late Majesty. Or the other way, maybe they need a loose hand to let them adjust. Mostly, it seems to me, they need to experience His New Majesty as His New Majesty will be, to feel his fit for the throne, his ability to lead them into a productive future, in their bones, in their necks, shoulders, pits of their stomachs."

He cut himself off, ready to stop. His New Majesty waved him on. "I apologize ahead of time, tremble as I say these words, just the fact of His New Majesty's lineage and naming as heir does not quite build the confidence they seek."

Princess Jo asked him to lift his head and eyes, to look at them as an equal, assured him he had not spoken out of turn, asked him to share any thoughts he had on how to accomplish the worthy goal he had laid out. HaOzer glanced up, shook his head, mumbled a denial of anything further to say, returned his eyes to the ground.

His New Majesty called on Ms. Tucker.

"Well, um, oh, and please forgive me ahead of time, Your Majesty, if I get the protocol wrong of how to address all of you, I hadn't thought I'd have a speaking role, did not prepare for it, yes, thank you, Princess Yehoadan for your understanding, all right, Princess Jo."

After sipping water the princess directed a staffer to bring her, Ms. Tucker suggested – not to contradict Reuven, she interrupted herself, who definitely had a better handle on the mood of the people – people might be worried about their voice as much as His New Majesty's.

"When you believe the Messiah is running your life – I'm sorry, I know, my qualifier invalidates all of you, as if I don't believe it. Allow me to be straightforward, with my advance apologies and the reminder I never intended to speak here: my bosses have forbidden me from ever giving the impression *I* believe His Late Majesty was the Messiah. A business decision, our viewers back home would never accept a flesh and blood Messiah, or watch a reporter who did. The *suspicion* I buy into it would destroy my credibility.

"They have no problem with my showing respect for *your* beliefs, we're tolerant people in NYC and the US. To make sure I don't slip, I have to always say it with the qualifiers, 'whom Israelis believe to have been the Messiah.' No disrespect intended, it's to keep my job."

She stood, "If that's unsatisfactory, I understand, and will excuse myself."

The table turned, some of the OC's faces anticipating a call for comments or suggestions from HNM, their mouths poised.

He instead said, "We do understand. Let Us table the issue of how you speak about Our late father for now, stick with the present topic. Please continue."

Surprised, flustered, she started what sounded like an apology, saw Princess Jo move to interrupt, stopped, composed herself, and said, "When the man you believe is the Messiah runs your country and your life, for decades, you worry less about personal cares or safety, because in your view he's the Messiah, you know? He has guidance and protection from Above, missteps maybe hurt you in the short term, you're able to tell yourself it's all for the best.

"He dies, first, you're shocked, much as you always *told* yourself he was human, much as he *said* he was human, you didn't fully believe it, he's a once in three thousand years figure! Ditto your reaction to his son, no offense to His New Majesty. Intellectually, you assume he's up to the job, you know he's been helping his father for years, his projects always garnered rave reviews at home and abroad, you hope and expect he, too, will merit help from Heaven.

"As a journalist, I say deep down, people are scared, and hate feeling scared more than we would expect, because they're out of practice with it. Items one through ten on their lists right now, find security. They might not admit it, might suppress any signals their bodies are sending them, might deny it when asked. Doesn't make it less true."

She stopped, Princess Jo asked if that was all, she asked whether that wasn't enough.

Then had one more thought. "In my experience, people feel reassured when they feel heard, when they have a way they can believe someone in power will hear and care to deal with their concerns. As they build confidence they'll be heard, see progress on the issues they raise, they start to develop an expectation of a warm, caring reaction. And that's ninety percent of what they want. If His New Majesty finds a way to help them feel heard, I guess I'd think they'll see him as a father/protector figure, as they did His Late Majesty."

As Recording Secretary, I admit I have taken liberties in expanding the Executive Summary. I will stop here because the plan into which the table digested HaOzer and Tucker's words became a matter of too public a record to bother with the ins and outs of the discussion leading up to it. I believe the part of the meeting I have presented will provide fodder for historians, political scientists, and philosophers for decades to come. I could not resist offering the first version.

The meeting broke up after His New Majesty told his communications advisers to draft and broadcast the announcement (reproduced below). His New Majesty set the next meeting for a week later, 8 Iyyar, 21 April, middle of Election Week, to review progress.

FIRST YEAR OF HNM HAZONIYAH, PALACE ANNOUNCEMENT 46

ELECTIONS FOR A RESTORED KNESSET

With the completion of *shiva* for His Late Majesty King Sar Shalom, the Royal Family forces itself to return to the world of the living. We believe our late king, husband, and father would have wanted us focused on the future of our august nation. As per recommendations from advisers to His Late Majesty, His New Majesty's own advisers, and outsiders, His New Majesty has decided to delay his ceremonial coronation until after a vote for and installation of a Knesset.

For Israelis younger than thirty, Knesset was the old State of Israel's legislative body, until His Late Majesty acceded to the throne. We recognize the suspicion likely to greet the idea, will not dignify it by laying out the ways people will assume the worst about the proposal.

His New Majesty has authorized this announcement as a way to record his commitment to granting significant advisory power to the reconstituted body. He commits to generally sign the laws the Knesset passes, adopt the policies they promote, enforce the norms they articulate as the will of the people – assuming they appropriately consult before reaching decisions, with him and others, and clearly strive to build consensus around what's in the best interests of the nation as a whole. He retains the right of veto, a power he plans to use sparingly.

Some will say the caveat undermines the endeavor, will be too certain a monarch would never willingly cede power. His New Majesty responds: Our people has always been a nation to tread its own path, and we intend to continue to do so. His Late Majesty, May We be an atonement for his repose, bucked opinion often, including in converting a democracy into a theological monarchy.

His New Majesty chooses to slavishly emulate his father in refusing to follow anyone else's path slavishly. His Late Majesty gave his son the gift of a blank slate, the ability to select and shape this Knesset's doings however he deems best, without need to amend, adapt, or alter existing institutions or political allegiances.

The Palace thanks the Sanhedrin and the office of our esteemed High Priest for deputizing some of their number as officials for Election Week. With the short window, the Sanhedrin and Temple do not have time to find the needed conference rooms across the country, and ask the public for suggestions. Please submit all ideas at electionoversight.org.il, ASAP.

The Palace recognizes the procedure for this election does not match democracy as practiced elsewhere. For those who wish to complain, the same site will have links and voice lines open for Election week, the two weeks of Triumvirate election, and the first two weeks of Knesset operations. Thank you in advance for your cooperation.

Absent updates, however, here is the process:

Regulations for Elections, New Knesset

Election week will commence this upcoming Sunday, 6 Iyyar, 5808, the postponed day of celebration of the one-hundredth Yom ha-'Atzmaut, Independence Day for the third State of Israel, second month of the 23rd year of the Messianic Era, 19 April 2048 in the world calendar. We recognize the brevity of the window, but the symbolism of the day, and its allowing us to complete the whole election in time for the holiday of the Giving of the Torah seems too good to pass up. We hope and thank citizens in advance for pitching in any spare time they have to make this a reality. Volunteers should contact their local court or priest.

Before or on the day, by 10am, all citizens shall choose a representative of a group of no fewer than ten and no more than twenty fellow citizens. Those representatives will, after 12pm, gather in groups of ten to twenty to choose one among them to represent them at the Hundred level, and so on, as laid out below. The expected tasks of those selected will be:

Represent the group to the next level, the representative of ten to twenty to be the voice of his/her constituents to the representative chosen by ten to twenty such representatives, and so on. [We assume the terms Ten-rep, Hundred-rep, etc. will become shorthand for the cumbersome "Representative of tens, hundreds, etc.". Citizens are free, however, to adopt other versions.]

Representatives will also be expected to initiate or further relationships with and among group members, taking the lead in building cohesion among what will certainly be random strangers at all levels beyond the Hundreds; foster enough comfort among group members to be able to jointly discuss issues, to feel safe enough to share policy perspectives, and to respect each other enough to value maximizing everyone's satisfaction.

There are three ways to choose Ten or Hundred-reps: citizens may sign a proxy (proxy signers may choose to bypass a Ten-rep, sign up only for a Hundred-rep); show up at the election sites with a pre-selected group of ten to twenty, to deliberate together over who shall represent them; or, citizens with only part or no group may ask the polling site staff to randomize them with nine to nineteen fellow locals, to deliberate and select a representative.

No earlier than 12pm, no later than 1pm, chosen Ten-reps shall be randomized in groups of ten to twenty to select one of their number to represent them at the Hundred-Level. For this selection, groups must deliberate for no less than two hours, to have time to get to know each other enough to make a well-informed decision.

No earlier than 7am Monday morning, election officials will inform Hundred-reps where in the district they should report, to meet their randomized group, to select a Thousand-rep. Such Meetings will start between 8 and 9am, and must last a minimum of four hours.

Tuesday and Wednesday will repeat the procedure, 7AM notification, randomized groups, Thousand-reps spending a minimum of six hours before choosing a Ten-Thousand-rep, Ten-Thousands eight hours before a Knesset member emerges.

It seems a long time, we know. We must all remember how hard it can be, how long it can take, to judge character. Wired to snap judgments as we may be, much as we may hold fast to them, we forget the nuances they miss.

Knesset members-elect will receive instructions on the further stages of the process, selecting committee chairs and candidates for the Triumvirate. All citizens will receive an explanation of the two-week campaign for the three top jobs, as well as a list of events to introduce the candidates to the nation, later this week. It will not start until the week after Election Week, to allow the hubbub over Knesset selection to subside.

The Palace and His New Majesty thank all in advance for their cooperation, and look forward to a formal coronation soon after the election. May the favor of Gd rest on us, establish the work of our hands for us.

GOSSIP! Buzz for April 17, 2048: Rachel Tucker Sighting!

Hey, *GOSSIP!* Buzz buds, welcome back to where you hear it first! Today, our *GOSSIP!* Buzz Israel tipsters have inside info on comeback reporter of the year Rachel Tucker, who we've been watching and rooting for this whole week as she preps us for the strangest election ever.

GOSSIP! isn't where you go for boring politics, we're here for questions like whether Rachel will again conquer our hearts and screens (uh, duh! It's like her sparkle brightens with time!). *We're* rooting for her, much as we all know ratings don't always go where we want (we still mourn Jackson Hinkley and his too-quickly cancelled *American Messiah*). We at *GOSSIP!* have lost good friends to occasional dips in ratings, too, we know it's a rough business.

Today, Rachel tripped our alert meters with her Sabbath shopping. Friday in Jerusalem's a busy time, markets full of people buying food and treats for the big Friday night and Saturday lunch meals, and snacks or a smaller meal later in the day. Someone of Rachel's stature, we'd expect her to have accepted invitations to friends or contacts, splurge for hotel meals, to cultivate sources at other tables and in the lobby scene, or hibernate with prepared food, resting up for a hectic week to come.

Nope, we have photos of her right there in the crowd (below and right, with thanks to the readers who have learned to wield their handheld's camera without Rachel noticing; forgive the quality on some, we've tried it ourselves, it's not easy), haggling over prices with the best of Jerusalem *shuk* veterans. Looks like she was planning to entertain, too, she bought enough for twenty people! Rachel Tucker, not busy enough reporting, cooking up a storm for a social set we wouldn't have thought she had time to develop!

Good Buzz, gang? Wait, we're not done, still haven't hit the paydirt part, what made us sure to share it pronto. *GOSSIP!* Buzz Israel tipsters go the whole nine yards, with extra yardage after the catch (to mix our metaphors)! *In* the market, Rachel was alone, on the way *to* and *from,* she had a mystery man on her arm (pictured).

All right, not *on* her arm, no PDAs in Messianic Israel, it's frowned on for married couples other than family events or airport reunions. Look at the body language, though, the two of them are leaning in the whole way, clearly more than friends. Who is he? We're working on it, and always remember, a published *GOSSIP!* tip, Buzz or regular edition, earns you $100 and a lifetime subscription!

The race to identify Rachel Tucker's new guy begins… now! Good luck, *GOSSIP!*ers!

Voice-Activated Audio Recording, The Temple Grounds

All right guys, let's do this quickly, candle lighting is at 6:30, and we still have to put the store in order for tomorrow night. I know some of you have been upset about Reuven for the past ten days, I wanted to give you a chance to get it off your chests, not let it fester or affect our work. Anyone want to start? Me?

Fine, I guess I know as much as any of you what's bothering you. Maybe I'll start by reminding you I've known Reuven the longest of anyone here, I'm employee number one, which also means the stock price affects me more than all of you combined. Not bragging, making a point if I'm comfortable with Reuven, you should think twice before complaining.

Second, pause and take a look at what Reuven's built here and in our other locales. You ever had a better job? One where you left work each day feeling filled through and through, exhausted from giving it your all, anxious to recharge, to do it all again next shift? If any of you have, go beg the old job to take you back, it's more special than any of you seem to realize.

It doesn't come cheap, building an institution like this. Not money expensive, life expensive. There's lots of reasons Reuven's never married – under intense pressure, by the way, all his family, teachers, everyone he respects, told him long ago it was past time he married – but the store's a primary one.

Shani Feinbaum said it to me, after one of their breakups: "I'm committed to my job, I work for *the Messiah,* for crying out loud, and I put in long hours, longer than Reuven's, I think. Doesn't make the store any less of a mistress to him. And sure, I've got my things or I'd have been married a long time ago, too, but Reuven? It's the Grounds."

You know Shani, you know she doesn't fabricate or exaggerate, you gotta assume she knew what she was talking about. Sorry, that about which she was talking. Happy, Noam? Yeah, it's not as funny as you think, less so each time you do it. Just saying.

And that brings us to Rachel Tucker. I was working at the store the first time, twenty years ago, no one had realized how serious it was for him. They knew she'd been around, everyone knew her name back then, knew she'd gone home, and knew Reuven was barely functioning. My job – barista/therapist, right? – was to take some of the management load off Reuven's hands, to give him time to heal, and while working with him on coverage, slip in opportunities to move him past her. He did all the work, is the truth, I think he realized what was going on, and pulled himself out of it.

Ever since, he's been, well, Reuven, dream boss, dream friend. And lonely guy. I had hoped Shani would be the one, hoped fifteenth time would be the charm. Not to be, and he seemed to sense if Shani wasn't it, no one would be.

Now Rachel Tucker's returned. Have you seen them together? Watch him next time, no, he's not a teenager, you're not going to see googly-eyes. Watch the almost-smile on his lips, the whole time she's around. Watch the crows' feet he's always refused to remove, how they deepen just slightly, like there's a joke on permanent replay in his head, he's heard it often enough not to laugh, still thinks it's funny enough to smile deep inside.

More than anything, watch the shoulders. Reuven carries himself a bit hunched forward, always rushing to the next task, always ready for the next problem. Those upper back muscles drop around her, he straightens, his breath comes slower, deeper, and clearer.

Why her? Who knows? Yes, of course she's beautiful, he's dated more than a few just as beautiful, none of them got a second date. And bright, and funny, and all that, so's Shani, for example. *You* don't have to see it, the point is, *he* sees it.

And if it means we have to pick up his load a bit for the next while, I think we all owe it to him. Any of you disagree, you're under no obligation to do more than the job, I'll find temps or other regulars willing to step in and step up. I'm making a doc right now, putting my name at the top for extra shifts if Reuven has to do something with Rachel.

Add your name only if you're able to go a bit extra, no judgment if you can't. Except one more thing: watch the two of them together before you decide. Not up close, from far enough you can't hear the words. Watch the smiles, watch when they lean in, fall back, when he bursts into laughter. Seriously, how many of you have seen Reuven cry from laughing?

If you still don't want to help, that's fine. Me, I'm all in for the two of them.

US Federal Government's Exhibit ZZQ-4, RICO Trial of Emilio "Eggs" Panitendi

[Phone tap authorized by warrant 123987566XLT, sworn by Judge Tony Gasparkelli, upon petition by Special Agents [redacted] of the FBI. Accessed by an FOIA request]

Mr. Panitendi, sir, Vinnie Ricciardi here. Yep, mom and pop shop corner of Paradise Rd. and E. Harmon Ave., good memory, sir, I think you *have* been here, soon after I first joined, I can't say enough how much I appreciate your accepting my application. My capo suggested I call because he's proud of my haul. I've built a pipeline into the U. of Vegas crowd, today I served what seemed like half the International Relations Department.

You know these academics, think books and small-sample studies tell them all they need to know about how people think. Perfect for us, they're sure they know how to bet, know the odds better than we do, can see where we've made a mistake.

Got pretty hairy, a bunch of them wanted to bet the farm, I wasn't sure I could handle the action, was almost going to lay off some of it, give it to our competitors, I know you want us to avoid trouble, and I know it's double the vig if we need a bailout from you.

System's the system, I'm not complaining, I'm telling you I knew the risk I was taking when I decided no way these pishers could predict a hundred Israeli representatives correctly. Sure, 1.2 million people come out of the first selection, how hard can it be to get a hundred right, right?

That's what they figure, cuz they're potzers. First, two thirds or more are being done by proxy, people don't want to waste their day off sitting around talking when they know the answer. Four hundred thousand left, still, my gut says it's going to break my way. I watched this Rachel Tucker woman interview someone from their palace, made clear how much the Israelis expect the picks to go off the usual political script, expect people will go for character, someone they can trust to care about and for all of them. A guy/gal who gets things done? They're a dime a dozen in Israel these days. She convinced me, I was pretty sure we were going to have surprises right and left. In every hundred selections, had to be three to four left field choices, was how I was willing to bet.

I'm thinking, Mr. Panitendi always tells us you can't make it in this business without a feel for it, I figure this is where the big boys step up and become men. My capo said call you, be safe, I know how much you wants us responsible for our own sheesh, call you away from your important business matters only for emergencies.

I figured a break here or there couldn't hurt old Vinnie's standing with Eggs Panitendi, am I right? Sorry, sir, I thought you had chosen the name, no, of course, Mr. Panitendi, oh, alright, thank you, Emilio.

Point is, boy did I hit it big – I mean we, of course, your cut's why my capo said you'd be happy to take my call. My quants named a thousand of the most famous, bettors couldn't choose more than fifty of them, any ninety others. They ate it up, were sure they knew better than some Wop, you know? No, they wouldn't dare call me that, I could see them thinking it.

We did have a few winners, you're always going to, the fun was it was none of the snot-noses from International Relations, because they didn't catch the trick of the system. Most of them picked the full fifty from the thousand, they were sure they had fifty guaranteed. 'Cept less than half the thousand made it, and not numbers one to three! Seems the political types, good at talkin to big crowds, ain't necessarily the best in a small room, where bull crap detectors are easier to fine tune, you know?

The head start put me way in the black, I was feelin pretty good. Rest of the day kept coming up Vinnie, surprise after surprise for them, money in the bank for me. Your cut, sir, from one day, two point seven!

Tomorrow might be quiet, I don't want you to think I'm hiding or skimming, people will lick their wounds. They'll be back, don't worry, take a few more rounds before they admit they have no idea how Israelis tick. If we're lucky, they'll keep telling themselves *now* they've figured it out, long enough to pay our grandkids' college educations.

Over the weekend expect a nice further uptick, gamblers will definitely be sure they can pick twelve out of 120 for Cabinet posts or committee chairs. It's the great thing about our business, people's egos won't let them give up, or accept they can't know.

Saturday afternoon our time, the Knesset announces three candidates for nationwide office, whoa! They'll be rushing back, because it's three people to fit in three slots, Prime Minister, who Chief Tech Officer, and who Foreign Affairs/Public Relations Minister, how hard can that be? Who'll be able to resist?

Six permutations, we keep the odds right, we'll make out like bandits, ha ha. We'll be taking them to the bank, sir, and I'll be thinking about how gracious and benevolent you are to have given me the opportunity. Hurray for this new king, Messiah. He keeps making us money, I'll call him whatever he wants!

Office Tapes, Leanne Conover, President, ABC News/Entertainment

[participant was made aware of taping in advance, consent form is on file]

Ms. Conover, thank you for seeing me. I didn't want a written trail on this, and you probably know I'm not one to trust Ryan, especially not regarding Rachel. So thank you.

I spoke to her last night, and she's struggling. It's a different country, we don't always credit how different people can be from each other, we're caught up here in America with emphasizing our similarities, to make sure we don't use those differences as excuses for prejudice. I get it, and as a woman of color, I want us to do more of it.

It leaves Rachel with the challenge of figuring out where Israelis are the same as us, to make them interesting to viewers, and where they're off-putting, aspects of their lives she has to be sure to keep out of her reports.

Right, find a local guide, exactly what the books say to do. The problem is, she *found* a local guide, and he seems to be perfect. A little too perfect. You know viewers and gossips, all they want to see is people getting together, they think love is the only thing that matters to the human condition, and that's putting pressure on Rachel.

Because she definitely doesn't love this guy, how could she, they barely know each other? She *likes* him, sure, she's not going to deny she likes him. But she has spent maybe two weeks with him, in her whole life. What kind of foundation is *that* for…anything?

She calls me last night after work, 9pm my time means she's either up really late or really early, she's freaking out. This guy, Reuven, he's her best bet for success, except she's decided she hurt him so bad the last time they worked together she cannot risk it again, would be unfair to Reuven.

I can't tell her what to do, but she did ask my advice, it's not unsolicited or anything. I try "tell me more," and she rambles about a Sabbath meal they had shared, six other people at the table, except she says he was the only one who brought up interesting topics. Every twenty-three minutes, when the pregnant pause hit, Reuven had something to spark them all up again.

Not all Israeli stuff, either. Sure – she said, her exact words – lots of it was Torah, no, ma'am, I'm not sure of the pronunciation, it's the best I remember how she said it, and then there was American sports, Chinese business practices, Russian winters. He surprised her with his breadth, she said, but is that enough?

I'm sorry, ma'am, I don't mean to contradict or disagree, I don't think I *am* rambling. Her success could be our success, and her failure might take us down the road of firing her, years of litigation over whether it was deserved, I think the network needs to have some advance warning over how it's playing out. My direct report? It's Ryan, ma'am, I made that clear at the start, and if he catches wind of any of this, he'll stop it in its tracks. I am hoping you'll agree with me such a course is not in our shareholders' best interests. Or our newroom's.

I'll try to be briefer. I said she was jumping the gun a *lot*, what did she need to know, other than he was a valuable resource with whom she was building a productive professional partnership? She says it's not professional for *him*, exactly the opposite, it's taking him away from his business, he's caught whiffs of grumbling among his employees.

She tells me it's a big deal, he's been there for his employees more ways than you can imagine, they're complaining, his new schedule's been a real shock to their system.

"Or they're not ready for someone like me," she says.

Ok, fine, here's my point, a hundred words or less. I said to her, aside from putting too much pressure on herself, all she needed was more time, let it grow or not, let it go wherever it was going to go. She's about to start worrying about how he'll take it, what he'll think, I tell her she's getting ahead of herself. She likes spending time with him? He's got knowledge she can use? There's no commitment in finding a way to combine the two.

Is she going to take my advice? You never know with Rachel, she can just as easily pull her own cat out of the bag or rabbit or whatever. I'm only saying, if she sends some idea your way, you'll know where it started, I hope you'll do your best to help it along. Because my own feeling is, the more we help her, the more she'll help us. She's got a few more blockbusters in her, our Rachel, we help her bring them out, we'll be better off. As will the shareholders.

Thank *you*, ma'am, I appreciate the time and the understanding.

Personal Ideas Map of R. Amittai Guvrin

Today's thoughts: In the morning study session, tractate *Sanhedrin*, I was working on our decision HNM was unable to leave the Palace for the funeral, checking if we got it right. Played with the idea he wasn't yet king, except it passes automatically, he was the only son in contention, no official need to anoint or coronate. Then I thought maybe he could forego his honor, choose to follow the bier, didn't see evidence, seems he's obligated to maintain a regal stance, part of inspiring awe in the rest of us.

You know my old saying, if at first you don't succeed, try, try, then put it away for a bit, no use knocking your ahead against a wall, the answer might come another time. I skipped to the legislative powers he's talking about giving the Knesset, shouldn't we be the ones to wield them? Wandered around the databases for awhile, plenty of sources on extradjudicial legislation, everyone quotes the *Ran*, didn't seem too much there one way or the other, seems like he has the right to appoint them as sort of advisers, his choice what to listen to, what not.

A day for drifting, then Reuven came by. What a fine boy, he's used his first fifty-some years so well, if only he'd settle down and have children. Too bad he and Shani Feinbaum could never pull the trigger, fine people, both. I thought it was one of his periodic clear-your-mind Torah study sessions, thought maybe we'd look at the pages on the obligation of childbearing, I gave up on subtlety with him a long time ago.

He had issues of his own, wanted to know the obligations of an employer to employee. I pull out the *Baba Metzi'a*, opening to the pages, he interrupts me! He's always listened when I speak, has let me go on as long as I take to reach my point, and then thinks and digests it before he asks his next question. It's so surprising, I close my mouth.

He surprises me again, wants to know does he have to show up to the workplace for them? If he's provided an environment where they can do their jobs, if the chain is functioning smoothly with the managers he's put in place, if his absence doesn't threaten their finances in any way, is he required, as the man who hired them, to be there as well?

I had never thought of it that way. Why *would* an owner have to be there, if he trusts the employees and they have the materials and leadership they need? My mind jumps to when my mother, ob"m, had lost it to the point where I could not care for her as she deserved, to take care of her properly, I would have had to treat her in ways not proper for a son. When we hired Mahalia, she could not have been more loving to Mom, and she could do whatever was needed.

I tell the story to Reuven, he doesn't see the connection, and the morning's study came back to me. Sometimes, I told him, the law's not the whole story, sometimes it's about handling life in the holes the law left for us to make choices. You hired them, what commitment did you make? Are they *used* to having you around, or you *promised* them you'd be around? What's changed, explicitly or implicitly? Have you helped them see what's changed?

And, because it's always important to throw it in, sometimes you get to choose, the law can go either way. It might be worth going down that road, find out what's drawing you away, why you suddenly have other places to be. And maybe explain it to them after you figure it out, they might be more amenable, it'll make it easier to find an arrangement that works for all of you. As I was saying it, I knew it was a sticky subject, because a guy in his profession sometimes gets used to his own rhetoric, might think a fifteen minute session with a barista is enough, where I'm thinking he might need an actual therapist to figure all this.

He gets my point, though, takes my referral, I hope he finds what he's looking for.

Me? Writing this shows me I spent the day on in-between spots, the interstices of law, politics, and society. Gd peers through the lattices, makes me realize today was a much better day than I thought as I was living it. I thought I wasn't getting anywhere, when I was getting a bunch more than I realized. Maybe tomorrow I'll be able to feel it while it's happening, not only in retrospect.

Intake Notes, Yedidya Arussy, PsyD, Specialty in Family Counseling

[Editor's note: The Allens credit therapy with saving their marriage. Before they signed the release to include these notes, they wrote, "Spreading Dr. Arussy's first impressions is a great public service, thanks for doing it. If it helps one couple, it's worth the loss to our privacy!"]

Be careful what you wish for, right? What therapist doesn't dream of a high profile case? People hear about it, confidentiality agreements or no, the satisfied couple speaks to their friends, they speak to their friends, clients for years. If it goes well. I'm recording right after, to be sure my impressions don't get lost or deformed by time and forgetfulness.

Met Braydon and Zahava Allen today, they're going to be quite the challenge, fifty-fifty odds of staying together feels a bit generous, maybe pie-eyed. And that's if all three of us make our best efforts, when either might throw in the towel at any time. Especially him, to his mind, he's the aggrieved one, going to take some doing to show him it's always a two-way street.

The danger signs: He's angry at her for what she did, angry at being dragged to me, sure he's the victim, isn't willing to listen to anything until she explains sabotaging him (his word).

She's equally sure she's right, says he's reaping years of neglect. Not a great start, right?

Asked them to tell me the story of their marriage, as they see it. Tough going, lots of interruptions, fights about details. Nearest I got, their story starts after his Hollywood career was over, he had lost a step in looks, had gotten many lifetimes' worth of wild oats out of his system. The good news was he had paid off any possible embarrassments, had no kids or baggage.

She knew his reputation, who didn't, she guessed he bothered wooing her because he'd had his fill of tens, was willing to go with – she laughed self-consciously, looked at him quickly for his reaction to her next words – a seven.

Good sign: he interrupted to say she had always been beautiful to him. Besides, he said, if Hollywood teaches you anything, it's how little looks matter. After a year or two, someone astounding in some other way will always come along, it's up to you to choose to resist temptation. Looks won't keep you together, only love will, he said, apparently an inside joke, she hummed the classic tune, he joined for a minute. Then, more good news.

"I never loved you in spite of your looks, I love how you look."

Then he gave the curvy, lopsided smile that enchanted viewers all across the world.

"Besides, a forty year old always rates a thirty-year-old a few points higher than thirty-year-olds would. By me, you were darn close to a ten, getting closer every conversation we had."

I held my breath. I could have seen her taking him to mean he thought he had once upon a time been better looking than her. She didn't, a reminder my job is to listen for how others hear words, not decide what they mean to me; she was *touched*, by Gd. I guess it's why they clicked, at one point, they heard what the other meant, regardless of how clumsily it came out.

They met when he was in Israel on a get-away-from-everything world tour. A real one, no one knew where he was, he didn't take meetings or post daily updates, wore sunglasses and a cap, grew a beard, all the camouflage from the spy novels. You can never prove motive, he gave every impression he was serious about taking time off from celebrity.

Somehow, he stumbled into a *yeshiva* – the two of them knew the story, didn't seem to think I needed to hear it. I didn't insist, first session's about building a general impression, not nitty-gritty. One of his teachers set them up, they dated for a year, the sticking point, back then, was where he would end up religiously.

"I didn't want to be a stop on his journey; he'd gone from zero to what felt like sixty in a really short time. I was there with him, unless he kept moving, we wouldn't be on the same page. I didn't mind his continuing for a bit, was happy to be a supportive wife for a year, I had a good job in town, none of it was a problem. As long as we had a plan for after."

Exactly a year after they married, she on maternity leave with their two month old, he launched the Braydon Allen Company. I had heard of it, who hasn't, didn't know what it does. I asked him to explain, said we'd extend the session, no extra charge, he spoke for seven minutes, I'm not much closer to understanding.

I *think* he built a pipeline identifier, came up with a better way to figure out the drugs that would pan out and how quickly, his investors mean he has the funds to be sure those drugs reach the patients waiting for them. At a nice profit for him and his backers.

I asked him how he thought of it, movie and web stars aren't pharma types. He winced at the stereotype, named actors I never heard of who *had* been at the forefront of tech, pharma could have been his thing.

Then he smiled, let me off the hook. "You're right, I wasn't the brains, I was the name and face, the guy who used to be Braydon Allen calls a pharma geek, he's gonna take a meeting, you know?

"A friend from *yeshiva* figured it out. He read companies' annual reports during the breaks from Talmud study, for the fun of it, and noticed each lab had its own code words when they presented their results. He studied correlations between… blah, blah, blah, yadda, yadda, he could tell who knew they had a hit, who was holding on to hope, who knew the jig was up, and could tell us when to invest, when to sell short. We were off and running, double digit profits every time.

"Sure, the labs and other hedge funds figured it out, the labs changed their writing style to avoid collusion charges. My guy's really good, always two steps ahead, on to the next loophole. Beauty is he loves it, he'd do it for free, it's the chase for greater insight that really excites him."

Braydon put up ten million for a fifty percent stake. Zahava says the three years he was building the company were her first inkling the allure of Torah study hadn't monopolized his attention, Braydon Allen dives head through toes into whatever he's doing.

She smiled as she remembered. "It's what made him so irresistible. For months, *I* was his project. It's addictive, like a drug. Then, wedding's over, you move to *yeshiva,* his *schedule* asks him to be away twelve hours a day, you figure, ok, it's *yeshiva.* The Braydon Allen Company told me, nope, it's Braydon, it's how he's wired."

It wasn't the end of the world, she said. She had work, a baby, the apartment they'd taken near the *yeshiva* had all her friends still close by. She wasn't happy seeing him only when holidays forced the office to close, but she could live with it, especially for the kid.

Then his biological clock went off, he wanted more children. She put her foot down, not until he took a golden parachute, had more time for them. She says she could not have been clearer the demand included a firm commitment on his part to be around more, an involved father and husband.

He said words she wanted to hear, although he denies any promise, stated or implied. For the six years of the next two's birth and toddlerhood, the children were his project, ambient warmth spread to her, made it – her word – paradise.

Fourth child was an accident, they both agreed. They seemed sure it was her fault, for reasons they didn't make clear, not vital to a first session. We weren't any nearer to the election fiasco, and I had cleared only three slots.

I had to put the question they were clearly avoiding.

She sighed. "I told him I was pregnant with Henna, I almost saw skid tracks. Oh, he kept up with the first three, mostly, outings two or three times a week. Time alone with me, or help around the house, disappeared. He had meetings, speeches to give, he was gone. My fertility was an unforgivable betrayal."

He had decided to fix Mitzpeh, the town they'd chosen "for a quieter life," Zahava said, with a bitter snort. He was going to find the solution to the water crisis, business development, factionalism. Took up all his adult interaction time. And energy.

She felt trapped. "How could I complain when he was killing himself for the town I had picked? At the company, sure, he had been helping drugs reach market sooner, at cheaper prices, but his skill wasn't unique, whoever bought his share of the company could do it, too. I made a calculated decision, knew he'd resent me for making him leave the company, was sure he'd eventually thank me for forcing him into a relationship with his kids. Now, he'd outflanked me, found an activity I couldn't oppose, still took him away from the house often enough we never saw each other."

She'd stewed, waddling around – her word – pregnant and with three little kids, he off reaping the praises of the citizenry and civic leaders. I probed gently, she was appropriately aware of the privilege in her problems, her financial cushion, the help of a full-time nanny *and* housekeeper, the boon of neighbors who were like family, of living in a place safe enough to let her kids roam the shared backyard or, as they grew, all over town.

She finished for me. "Yeah, yeah, and grandparents who moved to be a 45 minute drive away, far enough for privacy while also available for pop-ins. I get it, I have no right to complain." She sighed, smiled. "Braydon knew it, too, I had to admire his subtlety. After all, who other than a, well, you know, would find anything wrong with my life? What, I was upset my husband spent only ten hours a week with us, including three Sabbath meals, maybe an hour and a half alone with me, including any *really* alone times, if you know what I mean?

"What kind of needy harridan would harp at such a good man to be home more, as if she did not care about the people of Mitzpeh, right? Me, that kind and I hated how he'd maneuvered me into the position. Didn't make a difference, he kept doing what he wanted."

His New Majesty's announcement was tailor made for Braydon, the early sheets put him at 4-7 to make the Knesset, even money for the Cabinet. Zahava snapped, deep inside.

"His New Majesty's great kindness in allowing us representation, his unforced promise to pay attention to the people's wishes, to find a way to choose reps who had to listen to all their constituents, I couldn't let Braydon use his charm where he didn't deserve the job. Would have felt I personally was betraying HNM, the Lord should grant us many years of his healthy vitality. It would repay HNM's kindness with a kick in the teeth, Heaven forfend.

"I could have told him to find his Ten-rep group, I'd find mine, except I didn't trust anyone else to see what had taken me years. It's not that he lies, it's he shapes the truth misleadingly, and you only catch it when it's too late. I was up all that night – Henna helped, she was teething. By morning, I knew: we had to make him convince us, his wife and neighbors, he really intended to be there for *us*, to find out what we cared about, reflect that to higher levels, like the announcement said. If not, well," she sat up straighter, "it was my job and mission to help His New Majesty find *representatives*."

My training definitely affected how I heard her. To me, she was shouting how little she believed in him. The bad sign was it didn't faze him; he didn't care about anything she'd said, as far as I could see. What she had *done* had him fuming.

"Zahava's being honest, laying it all out, I'll do her the courtesy of doing the same. She can dress it up all fancy, it still all started with her tantrum about my not being there for dinner or bedtime as often as she wants. Trust me, when our kids grow up, if I give them approval and money, support whatever they decide with a genuine smile, they won't care how much I was around when they were kids.

"I know, because my father made that mistake. Gave up his career, supported my mother in her job, was always there for us, guess what? We went with Mom, she had the money, the power, smiled whatever we did!"

Mental cash register, he'd just given me a five sessions arc, two with him alone, two with her, one to bring them together, maybe more to follow up, be sure they'd learned better how to work with each other, an easy three thousand, not that I do this for the money. She was popping out of her seat to tell her side. I had to ask her to hold off, we didn't have time for digressions. Not right then, anyway.

"Braydon, you're the one who told me you have an emergency, yet nothing Zahava has said is, in your view, the problem. If it's not any of those, what *has* brought you here, on the brink of divorce, as you say?"

He let the question hang, like his head. The moisture in his eyes when he did look up might have been tears; I didn't offer a tissue, overreading a client's emotions is a big no-no.

"She should have *told me,* ahead of time, leave me to choose whether I wanted to try to leap through her hoops or find other options!"

An old fight, it turned out. He knew she was unhappy, thought they'd work it out over time. As long as she stayed out of his way, lived her life her way, let him live his way. She thought he spent too little time with the kids? Let her spend more time with them, he had enough money for her to stay home as much as she wanted. Or hire more babysitters, if she thought his absence tied her to them too much. He wasn't stopping her, she shouldn't stop him.

The mini-rant ended, "She didn't think I'd represent her? She didn't have to vote for me, it's a free country, but don't weave some half-baked story you and your friends want to build a great Ten-group, kick it off with a meeting instead of proxies, to sabotage me. I coulda had a hundred signatures like," he snapped his fingers, "been on my way. I'm good in a room, you know, it's one of my things."

He sat, back rigid, arms crossed, fury raw and fully exposed. Not my best therapist moment, asking a question without realizing its emotional valence. I let the silence sit, we all knew whose turn it was, her betrayal would be a tough nut to crack. I had to let her speak, then could maybe start them on their way back to each other.

As long as she did not drop any more bombs. She opened her mouth, I reminded her to recap what he had said, to be sure we had no misunderstandings, help him feel heard.

She waved me off. "I *totally* understand him, I *totally* see why he's upset. He saw his next great stage, was sure he was the magic the country needs, and I stopped him, deceptively. Right, Bray?

"Our problem isn't a lack of communication, Dr. Arussy, it's I didn't trust *other* people to see through him in one meeting. Like he said, he's good in a room, for six or eight hours he can be the most charming guy, there for you, caring for you, representing *you,* you'd never know he had any other ambitions.

"Until the moment the next rung in the ladder was in reach, he would hot potato anyone lower. He'd say it would all trickle down, the good in the larger picture will benefit everyone, to his mind means the peons have no right or reason to complain."

He muttered, "Well, it would, that's how life works, take care of the big problems, the little ones don't matter."

"Hah! You can't even get your Dickinson right. It's the other way around, take care of the *small* things, the big ones take care of themselves." She turned to me. "I couldn't be party to his deceptions, and as a wife, you're either part of the solution or an accessory. The only other option I could think of was a press conference warning everyone in my region. Would that have been better? Would it have even worked, or would people have dismissed it as a marital spat?"

She blew out a breath. "Most important, he's ignoring the key part, probably didn't notice it. I coached everyone before the meeting, made sure we talked up our shared backyard, how much we enjoyed our sort of extended family, how our barbecues – Bray wouldn't know about them, he always had important reasons to miss them – kept us in touch with one another.

"We were giving him a chance to see the value of relationships, to lean in to us as people. He only had to show us *something,* it's why we went four hours, double the other Ten-rooms, including the randoms ones. I kept finding ways to delay the vote, hoping a switch would flip. Had he"

It was time for her to address him, I said gently.

"Had you only said, 'Wow, I get it, I need to be better about this part of the job,' we would have given you a shot." She shook her head sadly. "Never happened, never a hint of anything other than confidence about how far you were going."

"People don't respect you unless you project confident!" he shot back.

It wasn't the greatest place to end, I do need to work on my pacing. Not like my lunch-gripe group, their stories always offer a neat bow, an insight to tide them over for a week. I couldn't find these two the one-week pass out of their prisons of anger. I gave them the best I had, reassurance I'd seen worse, belief our work could help them recover. It's definitely true for some couples, no way to know which.

They believed me enough to say they'd be back. I've signed up for supervision, I don't want my gut defeatism coming out. I'm thinking we have the first casualty of the election.

[Editor's Note: The Allens told me they've moved on from Dr. Arussy, are happy to report progress with their new therapist. The woods they're in are deep, dark, and dank, they asked me to say, they do finally see light at its edge.

They urged suffering couples to stick with it, not give up because the first therapist did not work. "You never know where or when the breakthrough will be," they asked me to say.]

Special Requisition Form 1073

From: Rachel Tucker, temporarily assigned to Jerusalem.

To: Budget Committee, ABC News/Entertainment

CC: Leanne Conover, President, ABC News/Entertainment as per (also cc'd) Shirley Beattie, Executive Producer and Direct Report

Re: Unanticipated staffing, expedited attention requested

Cost: Car with Driver, $2400 per week, Cameraman $3600 per week, or parts thereof.

Explanation, with prime alternative: The Arrival, as Israelis call the late Sar Shalom's conversion from Prime Minister to king, raised their standard of living higher than we're used to in the United States. *Much* higher.

They don't struggle to support it, either. Any staff I've looked into had equally lucrative options, seem to make their choices based on commute. They think they're doing *me* a favor taking work at the rates quoted. It's why I have to pay by the week, I haven't found anyone willing to pick up a day here and there, I'm told it's a pipe dream. I am asking for budget to pay a week's salary for the rest of this week, two weeks of triumvirate campaign, a week for the dust to settle.

After that, it depends on what HQ decides about continuing coverage.

As required by internal regulation 6628, I have calculated the cost of the most feasible alternative, poaching a current staff member from an affiliate, States- or Europe-based. The limited time frame makes the up-front costs more significant; for a six months' stay, the math probably tilts to existing staff, gives enough time for their later work to justify the learning curve.

Money aside, I believe we should prefer locally grown talent:

1) Local saves me the time of whoever we might choose from existing staff to pack up his/her current life and find his/her way here. Travel will not

be so easy or quick, there are still many grief tourists grabbing tickets to watch the country recover from its black swan blow. Certification might take time as well; with many Israelis taking compassionate time from work, licensing bureaus will likely be thinly staffed.

Each day counts, too, is a new stage of the election, and we'll miss much of it if I can't get around easily and quickly, without having to work about parking or trying to film myself.

2) Latest ABC guidelines allow a four-star hotel, $80 a day for food, in addition to US salary. Local talent ends up a bit less on this account, they charge less than a hotel, and will eat some home-prepared food. Figure $15 a day less.

3) The unpredictable cost of lesser quality. Experience counts, the best of foreign drivers will have to rely on the car's navigation system, likely miss a turn here and there because of unfamiliarity. It would be really bad, shall we say, if the particular turn comes right when I need to be somewhere for a story.

More, the car navigation system suggests what most people like to see around a particular destination, doesn't have an instinct or spur of the moment ideas for what viewers will find interesting, won't have its neck-hairs suddenly crawl with the certainty a detour might help me stumble on the one interview I wanted, or chance on a story like the ones I sent in yesterday, during Tens – and Hundreds-.

The best stories might be at opposite ends of the country, too, a non-resident will never figure out. Here more than anywhere I've been, life moves fast, and I'm learning, but having a local by my side would help.

4) I confess I have a particular driver in mind, will likely cost a bit more even than the estimates I've given, although I maintain he will be well worth it.

Full disclosure: Reuven HaOzer was a significant source for stories I filed last time I worked here, twenty years ago. Almost any search you make will imply we were more than colleagues back then, and I cannot completely deny it, although in the fog of time, who knows what we were thinking back then?

I am aware my apparent personal connection creates a presumption of suspicion around my suggestion to hire him, and I have brought it up myself to avoid seeming like I want to hide it. I believe my arguments stand up to objective outside scrutiny. Besides, the rumors make him a better candidate for the job. Who would work harder, make himself more maximally available, than a suitor hoping to score points?

He's also proven his value, too, he's the reason I'm the only newsperson – including Israelis – -allowed a tagalong on a palace *shiva* call. And don't try to pooh-pooh my exit interviews, they got great ratings even if Network did only put them online.

All Reuven, who also found me a way to be at the meeting where they decided to call elections. I can't say too much, secrecy laws, I *can* say I acquitted myself well on behalf of ABC, put myself on the inside track to become a trusted outlet for leaks to test the waters on future ideas. When they declassify the notes, I can assure you I'm going to be a hot ticket, every network will want my eyewitness take, I'd hate for it to be any network other than ABC. Again, all Reuven HaOzer. Who's also camera-genic.

I could argue we should hire him as thanks for the past few days, let alone the value he will bring in the future. I know you cost control types will say, if he's so great, let's do some stories on *him*, leave the confusing election behind. Show us Reuven HaOzer, you'll say to me, we'll think you're geniuses for thinking of it, if he's as well-placed as you say, pull on his thread, the rest will fall into place.

I've been doing this from when you were in diapers, maybe literally, it's a mistake, he's too well connected. Now I can hear you thinking, what kind of coffee shop owner has so many ins, whose money is he laundering? I admit it's how I would think about it in Vegas or Bed-Stuy. It's different in Israel, at the Temple Grounds.

I could tell you about it, but you won't trust me. So I'm willing to show you, come, make a quick trip here, it's 23 hours in the air, two in the airport or on the tarmac each way, an hour to and from the shop, an hour in – one muffin and coffee, a chat with a barista, you'll be a convert. And feel stupid for having wasted time and money checking up on me.

Because it's more than a coffee shop, more than pop therapy, more than the sum of its parts. It's where you go for a shot of confidence. You ever been to the Temple? It's a whole thing, my knees knock thinking about it, and people happily pay for fortification before they go.

Or, on the flip side, you gave life your all, it blew up in your face, Temple Grounds staff are great at helping pick up those pieces. Everyone who's anyone has passed through, the most complete discretion – Reuven's a fanatic about blocking, jamming, any kind of streaming or recording, audio, video, still. Windows are one-way, the whole works.

Walk in one time, is all I'm saying, you'll know how and why he knows everyone, why they all owe him favors. Favors he doesn't collect, he just always knows someone who's happy to help with whatever he needs.

Come. Or take my word for it. Sure, I could try to sneak a camera in, find out which anti-jamming devices I need, see how much I could film before he caught me. You want me to burn a valuable source forever for one story, max?

Convinced yet? Then get convinced, because right now, he's *excited* to work with us, thinks he's helping show the monarchy to the world in a better light. We don't want to push our luck, you never know when some new, more exciting project will come along.

He's already offered me a sit-down with the Assistant Head of the Sanhedrin, turns out he taught him in high school in Minnesota. Obviously, not during the madness of Election Week, I'll be too busy. Editorial will need to decide whether to keep me here longer, tape it after.

His cost will seem high to you, remember he's doing us a favor, charging us only what he needs to pay his replacement, promised to cap it at sixteen percent above what drivers usually cost, pay the rest himself, out of pocket.

I'm crossing my fingers on your wisdom.

5) Video Personnel *always* says hire local, ask them. Locals know how to film their people to look more American, our viewers prefer it. Video's got a manual, Company Memo A-122746, gives angle adjustments for filming foreigners. Because they figured out viewers' internal clock starts ticking as soon as a foreigner comes on screen. One minute in, give or take, they need a bathroom, snack, feel the urge to channel-surf, we lose them and advertiser dollars.

Israel has so many immigrants, local camera people know how to film all the types in all the ways, make Russians look familiar to the Swedish, British to the Chinese, you name it. *Seems* like it costs more money, saves on a separate angles' consultant and extra editing sessions.

5) Rapid response. I know you hate clichés, this one's truer than most: the next big story is *always* a surprise. Right cameraperson, with Reuven, we're there faster, with contacts to let us get closer to the story than anyone else.

The more scoops, the more we are viewers' go-to network. You always say, 'eyes and clicks, people, eyes and clicks.' Give me what I'm asking, sit back and enjoy the eyes and clicks.

Arrest Warrant Request, Fastest Track

From: Shin Bet, National Security Service

To: Honorable Rabbi Otniel Kalinski, Head Justice, Central Court, Ramat HaSharon.

We apologize for the inconvenience, assure His Honor we dithered hard – we didn't have time to dither for long, we had to pack it in to a few moments – before deciding the developing situation demanded we invoke the law allowing us to impose ourselves on His Honor's time.

His Honor likely knows the name Sylvan Rolatach. Although his hacking convictions all happened in other courtrooms (our lawyers tell us we may attach records of Rolatach's trials and punishments without consulting with him, as we have in Exhibit A, because they are uncontested governmental documents).

Statistics on recidivism (Exhibit B), combined with Rolatach's past, justify our petition to set aside the unlikely positive interpretations of the evidence. Mr. Rolatach is at the moment in the midst of deliberations in a Thousand-rep room in Hod HaSharon, said room may finish its deliberations as soon as an hour from now. We did turn to the court in Hod, all the sitting judges recused themselves, for reasons libel laws forbid us from divulging.

They relented only to authorize us to ask Your Honor to contact them, assured us they would be comfortable sharing with you what led them to decide they could not hear our claims. They also insisted on making our search warrants public documents, forced us to find a way to phrase them generally enough to misdirect attention from our true target. You have to bet a Sylvan Rolatach has alertbots trawling for law enforcement closing in.

The search warrants are Exhibit C, attached.

National Secrets Act 34235119 requires us to remind His Honor, before we may address Exhibit D, of the provision for immediate removal from office, life disbarment, and more, as punishment for unauthorized revelation of the computer records included there. As further background, we confess His New Majesty caught us more than a little off guard with the idea of elections; securing said elections, with one week to prepare, was especially challenging.

One concession from the Palace allowed us to insert tamper alarms into the programs randomizing the assignment of reps to groups. The ping in Hod HaSharon was our nightmare – we all knew the danger of a successful hack of the system. One person gets caught having done it, doesn't matter what happens to him or her, a thousand more will try, sure they'll do it better. The first person opens the door, lets the next hotshot be sure s/he'll find the way.

The Palace had warned us, repeatedly, of how much rode on reps having no advance notice of who would be in their room. *They* had wanted us to send the reps to their rooms blind, and only agreed when we showed them how complicated it would be to send them to the right location and then add a layer of bureaucracy for them to find their room.

They were focused on guaranteeing we could not get sucked back into party politics, influence-peddling, arm-twisting, blackmail, and worse. His New Majesty tasked his advisers with finding a process sure to weed out those kinds of people, elevate the people of good will, dedicated to representing all their people, in all their shades of opinion. Any opening to game the system, pick the other people in one's room, it'll be birds of a feather flocking, and we'll again forget everyone counts, not only those who voted for us.

It pains us to admit Rolatach's brilliance. He spotted and circumvented our firewalls, without us catching, packed his deliberation room with people he knew would like what he has to offer. We petition and urge His Honor to swear out an arrest warrant for now, before the vote; the optics of the government reversing a vote, the risk of being seen as trying to subvert the declared will of the people trumps a lot, we hope Your Honor will agree, is why this circumstance does not allow for the measured deliberation we ordinarily value.

Rolatach was smart about it, he did not pick known associates, he took from all over the district, threw in two true randoms. He almost got away with it, only his arrogance tripped him up. He stopped looking before he noticed we have a program in the system, checking for close links among the representatives in any room.

His region has 200,000 voters, meaning 2000 Hundred reps. Like many of his fellow representatives, he started looking into the background of all his fellow reps, nothing illegal about that. Like his fellow reps, he gave up somewhere around the hundredth, as he realized he could never research 2000 people overnight, had no way to plan a pitch tailored to each.

Honestly (and embarrassingly), he came up with a shortcut we hadn't thought of, searched the list for employees of companies he'd worked for. Seventeen from his district fit his bill, perfect for him, because he'd left himself backdoors in those systems. Lo and behold, he investigated ten of those seventeen for more than ten minutes each last night, and eight are now in his selection room.

Why would a computer security nerd leave himself open to such obvious detection, you ask? He didn't realize he was, thanks to our Comp CounterInt unit's success at keeping their latest secret, available for His Honor to view at our secure facility, if necessary.

We know His New Majesty's dedication to a hands-off policy on the meeting rooms, yet believe Your Honor should agree with us a Rolatach victory will be worse. A whiff of corruption, conspiracy theorists and cynics will decide His New Majesty manipulated the system to his advantage, Gd forbid.

The loudest purveyors of the theory, of course, will be the ones who worked the old system to their advantage. They will portray His New Majesty, Gd forbid, as insincere, faking interest in citizens' views while manipulating matters to produce a Knesset to his own liking.

Arrest Rolatach *before* he's selected, we believe a critical mass of citizens will agree the money transfers and communications show him buying off some reps, intimidating others. If Your Honor allows us, we can save the reps from themselves, from yielding to his pressure, can help them keep their record clean.

Is the innocence of eight otherwise fine Jews not worth the risk of others judging His New Majesty falsely negatively?

DESK OF OTNIEL KALINSKI
RAMAT HASHARON
RABBINICAL COURT

Ruling: Request for arrest denied, permission granted to breach selection room firewall.

Justification: His New Majesty, Gd should grant him and us a successful, long, and healthy reign, chose to re-install the Knesset His Late Majesty, departed Messiah of Israel, had disbanded. No one would have expected HNM to do so, he could easily have chosen to hold onto control of this process, directing queries such as yours to his Palace and offices.

He decided to leave supervision to the courts, released this new election into the wild, in a sense, kicked the hatchling out of the nest. We hear and heed his tacit call to make our mistakes and correct ourselves, rather than follow slavishly. To earn representatives, we must take the responsibility for selecting them well.

His willingness to tolerate missteps in the name of the people's owning the election tells this court we should risk a Rolatach victory. This court does not doubt Shin Bet's evidence, is impressed with their care for procedure and propriety at all stages of building the case. Shin Bet has convinced us Sylvan Rolatach is in the process of stealing a selection.

As Shin Bet itself recognized, however, there is a policy part to the question, weighing the loss in arresting him after he wins against the outcry if we rob the people in his room of their chance to choose. Granted, he is likely to win this level considering his packing the room. For all we know, he'll find lawyers able to convince a court he should be allowed to continue, perhaps lawyers skilled enough to win acquittal, let him take his seat in the Knesset or even Cabinet.

This court still finds the possibility preferable to any impression HNM was insincere in promising elections free of government intervention. In the name of full disclosure, this decision is influenced by this court's doubt he will make it anywhere near as far as Shin Bet worries. Wrong loses, with Gd's help. However it happens, at this level or a later one, His New Majesty's elections invite us to trust the process, to let the system correct its errors in the repeated iterations of selection.

Lest Shin Bet's admirable efforts seem a total loss, this court does authorize the request to breach the firewall around the Thousand-rep selection room in question, to forward to all the representatives in that room the executive summary of the files submitted to us, marking proven fact from not boldly and clearly.

Although I have been honored by my colleagues' certification as a Lone Expert immune to appeal, the sensitivity of this topic leads me to waive it. Petitioners should feel free to appeal, to the Great Sanhedrin directly should they choose, even should the current rep room render the issue moot by making their choice.

Our need for a precedent means this case should be adjudicated at the highest levels, no matter if events pass us by. Perhaps our seventy leading rabbinic minds will see nooks and crannies of the issue my meager intellect missed. Signed, Otniel Kalinski.

Appended to Judge Kalinski's File

BREAKING NEWS, Reuters/AP/UPI – Ramat HaSharon: In what locals call a shock, Shiffy Tzoreka has been chosen as Thousand-rep from Neve Gan, a neighborhood in Hod HaSharon. After selection, another rep in her room, Sylvan Rolatach, was arrested, charges still pending. Rumor claims he hit for the cycle, racketeering, influence-peddling, tampering, blackmail, maybe more.

Reuters/AP/UPI Israel was on the scene (we wish we could take credit for our brilliance in putting ourselves there; obviously we cannot, there were too many selections for us to have hit upon Hod HaSharon. Our tipster insists on anonymity, but has received the promised gift card to P.C. Richards Herzliya, with our thanks for helping us perform our civic function).

None of the reps would discuss Rolatach, would not confirm or deny contact with him prior to entering the selection room. Shin Bet spokespeople did proudly tell us some of the reps had agreed to turn state's evidence. On the record, reps spoke only to Tzoreka's qualities. A random sample, none offered for attribution:

"I've known Shiffy for years, she's the one organizing neighborhood events, makes sure everyone can join, the one finds the homebound, brings them out of their shells, self-imposed or not. I would never have voted for anyone else, pressure or no pressure."

"My mother lives a block away from me, always teases me Shiffy calls her more than I do, or any of my siblings, gives her a more sympathetic ear than us all combined."

"Shiffy's barbecues? Legendary. I found my last three jobs there, same as my friends. She's a lifesaver."

The closest this reporter came to an ordered presentation of what had happened was in the words of one Hundred-rep. To hide his/her identity, we will use initials, EAS: "She is the kind of person you have to vote for, no matter the risk, jail, a beating, your family. If you're going to go down, might as well go down doing the right thing."

Congratulations to the people of Neve Gan on finding such a representative, and many good wishes to Ms. Tzoreka on her future selection rooms, with best wishes we see her in His New Majesty's Knesset, or higher. She's one to watch!

Transcript of Phone Conversation, Handheld Number 972545556470

[Note: Signs all over the country make clear the Israeli government records all international communications. The government says it seeks to imitate Gd by reminding all residents and visitors there is an Eye that Sees, an Ear that Hears.

Transcripts can be accessed only by passing the high bar for a warrant or securing consent from the parties. I thank Shirley Beattie and Rachel Tucker for consenting to my including it here, sparing me the arduous process of proving the purity of my motives and the validity of use. I present the full transcript, unedited for clarity, concision, or relevance.]

Shirley: Hi, Rachel, it's Shirley.

Rachel: Hi Shirley, what's up?

Shirley: I'm looking at this Reuters story on Hod HaSharon, did I pronounce it right?

Rachel: No, the first word rhymes with code, perhaps a little softer on the 'o'. And 'HaSharon,' the two 'a's are each 'ah,' and the last 'o' is like in 'old.' It's a confusing language, I'm making progress, especially with place names, it helps me with interview subjects, I sound more like I belong.

Shirley: Ok, great, thanks. (silence)

Rachel: Is that what you called for?

Shirley: (laughs) After what, eight years working together, you really think I called across the world to check pronunciation? I'm pretty sure I have fact checkers for that.

Rachel: Why ask me, then, first thing?

Shirley: Convenient distraction before the business at hand.

[Ok, this clearly doesn't work; the rest of the conversation *has* been edited for clarity, concision, and relevance. I left the first bit in so you know I tried to stay out of it, I'm doing this as a favor to you, you don't have to slog through their entire conversation. Of course, some of you won't trust me to have presented it accurately, will assume I'm putting my own spin on it. Can't please everyone.]

I'm calling because I'm not the only one here wondering why we ok'ed your high-priced help when Reuters apparently beat you to the punch by offering *gift cards to P C Richards,* fer Chrissakes. I sure *hope* you haven't played us into funding your dating life, with no upside for us. I'd hate for Ryan to turn out to be right after I lobbied to have him sacked.

And don't think – -

Rachel: Whoa, whoa, whoa, Shirley, slow down, why so upset? I missed *one* low level story. Sure it was the best one of the day, it's bound to happen. Hell, Reuters, UPI, AP, they *said* it, with 12,000 selections, *none* of us could guarantee we'd catch the best stories!

Don't even say it, I can hear you in my head, well then, what's Reuven worth? First off, *you* told me to take a flier on finding a way to spend more time with him, maybe figure out what the two of us have. On the pure business side, I filed five stories today, three you thought were good enough to broadcast, don't pretend you were doing me a favor, those were solid stories, and the other two are in the site's top fifty downloads for the day. With double the network percentage of new viewers, guest log-ins, clicking from a search for *my* stories.

I'm making inroads, is my point, building a viewership. Sylvan Rolatach's arrest was the most *sensational* story of the day, I grant you, doesn't make it the most *characteristic* one. Those other news groups, they don't have Reuven's advice, they'll throw resources at Shiffy Tzoreka, track her the rest of the week, sure she's gotta be something special because she beat Rolatach in a rigged room. Reuven says I can safely give five to one she disappears into the woodwork. One rep said it well, who cares about *any* of these people, there are *twelve thousand* of them!

I agree, it's not flashy or sexy to watch Israelis spend hours finding the person best able to listen to them and find common or middle ground when compromise is impossible.

I did like this quote of hers, "How'd I win the room? I said to my fellow reps, I'm going to work where we already agree. Everything else, slap a band-aid on it, it'll get infected, we'll have to come at it with more cooperative eyes." Story of this election, our viewers haven't caught it yet, they still look for arrests and scandals, we're making headway, story by story, showing them Israel's going a different way.

Shirley: (sighs) I might have guessed you'd tell me to learn to be patient, they have you drinking their Kool-Aid. Not as easy with your job on the line, you know.

Rachel: Tell me about it.

Shirley: No, way too dark a turn to hang up now. Pause for positive pick me up. Tell me about Reuven, non-broadcast. Eight years I'm spilling about my ups and downs with Rahim, your turn, missy!

Rachel: My turn to laugh, Shirley. You don't overcome twenty years of being apart in two days of car time, other than in romance novels. And no, I'm not being coy or secretive, it's… well, maybe I'm missing the rom-com gene. I know, you want the stories of moments we're coming closer, you want me to paint a picture of what draws us to each other.

I do wish, a bit, I was the type to meet a guy, be instantly sure, the couple falls into each other's arms forever as the music swells and you cut to waves crashing on the shore. It's not going to be our story, least not mine. We have good patter, it came back right away, that's good.

Other than that? We're learning, what we like, what we value, how we operate, how we take care of people who matter to us. Or I am, I assume he's doing the same. Unless he *is* one of those romantic types who leaps based on vague feelings. I hope he's not, it might be a deal-breaker. And we have to figure it all out while churning out stories, adding a degree of difficulty.

Shirley: Oh, Rachel, you're always so Rachel! (Laughs) I say it with love, we all love you for it, Rach, I hope it works out, but it *can* be frustrating, how good you are at bringing other people's stories to life, how little you tell about your own. Give me *one* nugget, can't you? *Something* must have happened, from when you hired him, hints at the future?

Rachel: Ok, for you. I'm turning off video, your face will tell me what you're thinking, I can't risk seeing you thinking I'm a big moron, I think it too much myself. Ok, we're in the car, it had been a long day, Reuven found five Thousand-reps to tell us on the record how they won, made my day mostly busy work, point the camera, ask a softball question, away we go.

Took us the whole day, they lived in places an almost perfect pentagon of the country, eight hours on the road plus a half hour with each, takes time to build enough connection for a worthwhile five minute interview, my viewers know I don't foist pap or fluff on 'em.

Shirley: Rachel, Reuven? I do have a meeting…

Rachel: Right, right. We're headed back to Jerusalem from Arad, forty-five minutes on the new roads, exhausted in the way you feel after a productive day. Outskirts of Jerusalem, I think my mind had literally nothing in it other than shower and sleep. He stops the car.

Shirley: Buys you dinner?

Rachel: This is ten o'clock at night, we ate long before.

Shirley: Flowers?

Rachel: If it were *you* in the car, and he was the kind of guy *you* might have a future with, he'd have been the kind to cap a day with flowers. Still guessing or my turn?

(Pause)

Shirley: Oh, sorry, your turn. I was rolling my eyes and hands, I forgot you shut the camera.

Rachel: He ran into a store, bought blankets and hot cocoa for some people he saw sitting out, watching the stars. Said he used to star-gaze himself, remembers the nights he forgot supplies, couldn't bring himself to miss a moment of night sky, almost froze to death.

(Long pause).

Shirley: And?

Rachel: No and. I told you it wasn't worth telling. I looked at his face when he came back to the car, he was flushed with happiness, maybe pride. (Laughs self-consciously) It was a moment, that's all.

Shirley: You win, it wasn't worth telling *me,* for sure. If it worked for you, more power to you. Mysteries of love, I guess. Shows me a thing or two about assumptions.

Rachel: (laughs) Good night, Shirley, better stories tomorrow, on air and off.

Diary Entry, Amir Ovadyah

Some are born to study partners, some achieve study partners, and some have study partners thrust upon them. I always felt Reuven was my good fortune, I land a job at the flagship store straight out of training, then he asks me to study together in the downtimes, only way either of us will manage to find regular portions of the day. Sounded great.

It mostly has been, today was a slog, first one in a while. He said he was exhausted, I can agree that was part of it, definitely not the whole story. His mind wasn't in it, and his is not a mind you can force to be in it when it doesn't want to. It's like, imagine making someone read the whole sermon on Jonah in *Moby Dick*, I can't imagine it, these were fiction readers, why would they want to read a sermon? Let alone now, what high school would think of trying to get students to read it, when they don't even *go* to sermons anymore?

Point is, we're studying the court system. We figured we send practical questions from the store every day, in staff review, we learn practical rules from the rabbi's answers. He and I, we wanted to study something more theoretical, remind us it's about more than practice.

Today he walks in, says he wants to maybe pick up laws of marriage or courtship or seclusion, I say no, that wasn't our agreement. He's annoyed, I can tell, except he can't admit it, part of his whole persona is he's conquered his ego, is close to conquering his anger.

My mistake, because we spent the whole time talking about Rachel Tucker anyway. Oh, he'd never say her name, he kept arguing we hadn't paid enough attention to how men and women interact when we set up the store. How maybe the baristas should gender segregate, men counsel men only.

It wasn't him talking, it was whatever is worrying him. I made the mistake of trying to reason it out with him. I pointed out we had checked our setup with the rabbi, and anyway, we had set this time aside for *theory*, not practice.

The mistake was thinking he was speaking from his mind or brain or whatever. I guess I'm so spoiled by his excellence in filtering his emotions to see which are justified, to see him letting his emotions run the show like the rest of us was unsettling. Didn't bring out my best self.

I'll apologize tomorrow, we'll study what he wants to study, I hope he's not far enough gone to think I have useful advice about this woman. If he is, he's been there for me when my mind was fried more than a few times, I will have to do my best.

Then maybe we can get back to real Torah study.

Special Election Supplement, *Northern News and Times*

Wednesday, 9 Iyyar, 5708, April 22, 2048, Page Seven

Messages of Honor and Support for Ten-Thousand Rep-Elect Yevgeny Sapozhnik of Ma'alot Tarshiha, number twelve from Northern District

Posted by: Veterans of the Turkey War, Unit 4720

The "Rush-the-Ramparts Gang" congratulates Yevgeny Sapozhnik – light of our unit, ringleader on our best pranks, ear for our problems – on his elevation to Ten Thousand-rep. Almost half the citizens of Ma'alot-Tarshiha chose people with the good judgment to spot Yev's excellence – we salute their acuity. We had some great times with Pozh, as others of us called him, and assure Ma'alot-Tarshiha they can expect more of the same.

A special thank you to our unit commander, Leead Gorieli, who convinced Yev it was time to put the war behind him. Ten years of taking odd jobs around the neighborhood, filling in where employees had called in sick or a seasonal uptick meant a temporary shortage, ten years of winning hitchhiking contests across the country, enough, Lee told us he told Pozh. More power to him for telling it like it is, more power to Yev for finding his way back, more power to all of us who will benefit from a more involved Yevgeny, starting with the people he'll rep.

Hats off, bottle raised, all hail Pozh!

A PSA From PTSD Israel

Congratulations to Yevgeny Sapozhnik from his friends and brethren in the Mount Meron chapter of PTSD Israel. Big Pozh, as he's called by all who know him from meetings or the countless events at which he's volunteered since his release from hospital. PTSD Israel takes this opportunity to remind the public damaging stress happens in places other than the battlefield, is not limited to heroes who rally a decimated squadron to overcome heavy artillery to achieve kill ratios of thirty to one, with only light arms, knives, and hand-to-hand combat skills.

When we are overwhelmed, there's no reason or need to feel guilt or shame. Trauma hits each of us differently, honesty is the most important part of the solution, telling ourselves the truth about where we are in our mental health journey. Or, as Ma'alot-Tarshiha's new Ten Thousand-rep has often said, accepting ourselves and others is the first step to recovery.

The rise of a survivor with the courage to share his struggles with the public is a boon for our society; Yevgeny Sapozhnik's competence and qualifications are obvious. More, his model of recovery will help especially those of us who suffer as he did.

For all those fortunate enough to have not yet been brought to their knees by life, please know his success helps remove the stigma many of your friends and family feel every day. Thank you, Yevgeny, and may the good Lord reward your hard work in full!

SBA of Ma'a lot-Tarshiha

The Small Business Association of Ma'alot-Tarshisha congratulates Yevgeny Sapozhnik on today's victory. We struggle with our very seasonal economy, tourists, agriculture, peaks and valleys. A worker like Yevgeny, happy to take random shifts at three and four places of business during busy times, without complaining about down times, has been a kindness far beyond the wages we can pay.

A man of his talents clearly did us a favor putting his life on hold as he did. We thank him and wish him well as he moves onto the larger platform he richly deserves.

The Ten-Thousand Rep-Elect Himself

I have had many doubts in my life. Losing two thirds of a leg in the Bosporus felt like a slap from Gd for longer than I choose to remember. It has taken me more than the average length of time to feel blessed the explosion did not kill me, to see the Lord's kindness in saving me, in giving me the resources to take the time and space I needed to heal.

Beyond bare survival, finding my dear Yardena in the worst moments of my meandering recovery was surely a lifeline from Above, although I confess it took Yardena pointing it out to me, during an argument. My thank yous therefore start with Our Father in Heaven, not only to conform to convention. As King David taught us, I will thank Him with my whole heart, among the righteous and congregation.

I could do so fairly privately, in prayers, or in public speeches. I write here to thank the many messengers Hashem saw fit to send to help me find my new path:

To my parents, siblings, and the spouses and children they brought into my life: Thank you for the "family reunion," where you surprised me with proxies making me a Hundred-rep without lifting a finger. A finger I surely would not have been wise enough to lift myself.

To Yardena, for talking me down from my anger at how they manipulated me, who opened my eyes to the love and respect being showered on me, a hundred people risking their proxies on a good for nothing who might turn down the job, or fall down on it. Thank you for the freedom I needed these trying and worrying years, and for occasionally joining me on a hitchhike around the country. May the Lord bless you with a happy future, and may we merit to spend much of it together, as we marry and begin our lives for real.

To the Hundred-reps in my Thousand-room who let me ramble on about how healing it had been for an above-the-knee amputee with PTSD to find employers willing to accommodate an erratic ability to work, to provide enough odd jobs, at odd seasons, to keep me alive and able to support my travel therapy. More than the ear, I thank them for showing me the positive in my stories, the people skills I hope they were correct to claim I have developed.

To my colleagues in the Ten-Thousand room, thank you for your trust. I did not and do not take lightly your willingness to weigh my life experience equally with others' distinguished years in Torah, politics, education, law, or as entrepreneurs. Each person in each of my rooms had a more impressive resume than I could hope to assemble; I am humbled by your confidence. It has lit a fire of hope I might be able to reward your instincts.

If I succeed, and our lives move in ways we all would hope, much of the credit will go to His New Majesty, whom I thank for allowing us to choose a Knesset. May Hashem continue to send light and insight to HNM, his advisors, his government, including whichever of us are selected tomorrow as

Members of Knesset.

May we all see our paths clearly, and walk confidently into our future.

Quarterly Leadership Meeting, ABC News/Entertainment, April 22, 2048

Recording Secretary: Jane Wexler

All right, ladies, enough with the private gabfests, let's come to order, time for our spring installment of What's Going Right at ABC News/Entertainment? I'm sorry, and gentlemen, congrats to the three boys who have made it to our august table! Welcome, gentlemen, we hope you enjoy our little tete-a-tetes. You've made it this far in a woman's world, you can probably follow what we're saying, what we're *not* saying, wink, wink, what we're implying.

It's been awhile since we've had to adjust ourselves to male sensibilities, we'll try to do our best. But if any of it is over your heads, catch me or any one of us after, we'll catch you up. Maybe take you out to dinner, if you're free, you boys have done a fine job of staying in shape while running this rat race, and we all do appreciate a man in good physical condition.

Yes, Julie, I know the calendar calls our meeting What's Going *On* at ABC News, I don't like it, it's too neutral. Someone might read the name, think we're here to hash out negative events, too, post-mortem the hiccups of the past three months to death. Can't be done, it'll definitely leak, other outlets or any of our own people hot for a scoop, boom, it's out there, we can't get it back – doom and gloom, ABC News is going down the tubes, stock price dives, panic sets in, we'll all be toast, for nothing. We like to be positive here at ABC, am I right?

It's why *I* call our meeting What's *Good* at ABC News? If we have time after reviewing all the good, finding ways to build on the successes, I'll open the floor for nitpickers. Start with bright spots, I say, and I'm sure it's why I've risen the ladder here, people like my positive approach, my California girl sunniness.

You're right, Corazon, we can't hide our problems, anyone *can* access the ratings and clickthrough numbers. Yes, if they start pulling on those threads, they'll get the story we're not telling. Experience tells me if we give them an open and honest presentation of what's going right, they won't bother, so why do their oppo research for them?

No, Wendy, let's not start with *Ice Road Spitballers*, if we discuss it too early, everything after will feel like downhill. I want a bright spot, not blinding glory. Here's a good one, Rachel Tucker. If you consult the chart on your screens, I think we can agree to celebrate her remarkable progress. Her five minutes last night drew double her total for the funeral and the mourning visit to the Palace combined. *Double*!

What's she learned, what's driving the better numbers, how can we spread her insights to the rest of our teams, especially our international correspondents, who also have to translate a culture for our viewers?

Good, Zadie, she knows no one wants to hear thousands of results, it's too much, and they definitely don't want their newsperson mocking them for choosing to stay ignorant, absolutely right. She's giving them exactly what they want, quick, digestible dramas they can share with friends next time they're out for coffee, help them feel smart and informed with minimal time and energy.

Not a bad stab at a slogan, Morgan, only slightly too long: "helping people feel smarter, without having to pass a graduate seminar." Maybe: "Feel smarter, without the grad work!"?

Oh, yes, right Nellie, I did want to send a note to her producers, thanks, and yes, we should write it together first. We're getting a lot of contact from viewers, mail, e-mail, social media, honing in on Reuven, anyone have a problem if we tell Rachel's people – what's her director's name, Shirley Something? Beattie, that's right – to put him on camera more? Well, Yolanda, try it yourself, go to last night's piece, I think Reuven first enters at 1:42.

We all love Rachel all the time, of course, except look at her face before and after. Exactly, she lights up. I had an intern watch all her reports from there, in case it was a fluke, she confirmed the stats. With Reuven on camera, her eyes are two shades brighter, her smile opens three millimeters wider. Bantering on the phone, a shade and a quarter. He comes on camera, she's ablaze.

And when Rachel Tucker's lit up, well, I don't have to tell you, we've been living off her for years, it's like the song says, she can turn the world on with her smile. Make a nothing day all seem worthwhile, you can hum the rest to yourselves.

Of *course* I don't mean to dismiss him as "only" a catalyst, Gwen, none of us girls do. And gentlemen, yes, you're right, George, if Reuven sends the same thrill up your spine he sends ours. A man like that's never only a catalyst, he makes Rachel a better newsperson.

I *do* love how he always says, "Wake up and smell the coffee, Rach!", you're right, Kelly, it's either remarkable instincts or someone taught him how much people snuggle up to the comfort of predictability, the way to make them feel safe enough to engage with the new and unfamiliar. That's it, George, now you're getting it, Reuven helps them tolerate uncertainty, catch phrases help us dog-paddle through information without drowning.

Good question, Ryan, I'm glad you're the one who asked. Who *did* sign off on paying Reuven's exorbitant fees? Oh, wait, Ryan, they're *not* exorbitant because he's worth more than every penny, the ratings jump he gives us.

Makes me wonder why we're paying *you,* Ryan, easily a more exorbitant salary than his, especially when I have reason to think you've been sabotaging our Rachel. How do I know? Sorry, whistleblower protocol, your lawyer can read it in a secure facility, after she promises to hide the whistleblower's identity and after you accept suspension until resolved.

Oh, and yes, I did invite you here today to give you a chance to make me doubt the whistleblower. Sad for you, you went the other way. Why don't you take the rest of the day off, we can meet tomorrow, my office, 7am, figure out our next steps. Not a problem, delay the massage until nine, we'll be done by then, and you'll need one.

Sorry for the little unpleasantness, everyone, I needed a trail before sending Ryan off into the sunrise. Ok, who else has ideas for how Rachel can build on the great foundation she's laid? I'm not sure, Diane, if we have time for a full brainstorming, Shirley needs to share our thoughts with Rachel before she goes to sleep, they're hours ahead of us over there.

More road reports, Jill? Excellent idea, I like those, too, they're interviewing a winner in Haifa or somewhere and a tip comes on a breaking story in Safed, the hour we spend with them on ABC Live Stream is gold. They're at their best unguarded, unedited. *And* we get good crossover, Live Stream viewers checking back to see how it turned out.

Wandering a town after the end of the day, where they stumble onto stories separate from politics, it *is* the best, Jill, focus groups agree with you, and yes, they do single out their repartee, how they turn an aimless trip into special moments.

Imagine an American living in Israel, or in Wichita with two degrees of separation from someone in Israel. You're watching this crazy country roll the dice on a government, you gotta be stressed. We give them an attractive couple, whose random steps work out ninety percent of the time, it calms them, helps them believe it will all work, despite whatever no-name lucks his or her way up the ladder.

Remember when Rachel heard about a group protesting Ma'alot's Ten-Thousand rep, who wanted HNM to stop his candidacy, worried a washed-up war hero whose biggest claim to fame is winning the hitchhiking award five years running would be their new Prime Minister? When she profiled him, she did us all a service, helped Israelis be more comfortable with the future, showed us all how overblown our worries can be.

Doing good while making good, people, it's honestly why I got into this business. Anything else? No. Then, unfortunately, we have to talk about *Real Housewives of Ozark*. I know we never thought we'd see this day, it might be time to admit it's run its course...

Barista Supervision Meeting, The Temple Grounds

Ok, people, you asked, he responds. I told Reuven you all had missed his input at our last three meetings, and here he is. Fire away with your questions and scenarios, you've got the ear of the master himself. Don't laugh, I'm not joking, I've been doing this for seventeen years, I have situations crop up *all the time* I bring to Reuven.

Sure, ninety percent of people's problems get much better with a simple airing out, I'm aware of it much as you, we bank on it here. Listen, nod, put in an um-hm here and there, five-star rating more often than not. I know some of you think it's all I know how to do.

It's not. There's plenty of times the person lets slip the real problem without realizing. What? Oh, either one, without realizing he or she had let it slip, more importantly without realizing what the real problem was. An example? Hold on a second, let me think of one where the details aren't essential.

Ok, I have a guy comes to me all hush-hush, people know him, he's worried about other patrons in the store seeing him talking to me, thinks it might tell people he's having problems. Yes, it's a he, how much does that give away?

Anyway, he *says* the problem's his business, he's been having conflicts lately, has had to be away more than he ever has in his decades running it. Word gets out he's not around as much, he's worried competitors will think they can step into some power vacuum, investors will think he's pulling out.

So, gang, you tell me, what's my next move? Right, good, of course we go to the back room for privacy, I tell the staff to turn on the camera, to avoid any misunderstandings later about what happened in there. Good, fine, we sit down, he thinks he's told me the problem. Has he? No? What do I need to know? Excellent, I would come around to asking what was drawing him away more often, it's where he let slip the real problem. Wasn't my first question, anyone know why not?

Sorry, what's your name? Hailie? Excellent, Hailie, good instincts. I *did* first ask what made him sure the business would suffer without him, it's always a question to ask, most of us overestimate our importance. And if he's right, one part of the answer might be to find or train someone who really can take over the business when he needs to be away.

He says it's in the works, not simple, his business sits in two or three niches at the same time, you have to know all the sides of it to be able to run it, can take years to get a full handle.

Exactly – how many years? Sure, no one's going to know it like the founder, but… Part of his problem, for sure, he's a little too possessive, almost like he has nothing else going on. We all agreed? Good, he agreed, too, progress, opens the door to maybe take him the next step.

I ask him what's so important to start pulling him away, we can all bet we know, right? Yep, it's a woman, and this isn't some twenty-something. She needs his help, it's a complicated situation, he doesn't say too much, I can't say any of what he told me, point is, he's stretched, employees are complaining about his work, he wants my advice.

What's my next move, gang, a week's pay to whoever figures it out. *I* didn't have to ask any more questions, because there was background I can't share with you for the purposes of this exercise. You've got all the clues you need, a man with a problem about his business, isn't facing his real issue. What's the issue? What should he do?

Reuven? What about him? Oh, you want to know what he would do? Reuven, what would you do? Are you blushing? There's no blushing at The Temple Grounds, everyone here knows there's nothing to be ashamed of or embarrassed about. Excuse me? Yes, I suppose Reuven blushing *is* a clue.

What's your name? Varda? Well done, Reuven *did* want advice on how crazy his schedule has been, didn't know how to bring it up, I suggested this little subterfuge, kill two birds with one stone. Because, yes, Reuven HaOzer thought it a question of how to run the business, live up to his commitments to all of you, when I bet all of you immediately noticed it was about – call it out, don't be shy.

Yep, figuring out what might be possible for him and Rachel Tucker. Still, he worries you resent his absence. What say you?

Now do you believe me, Reuven? *We've got this.* The Temple Grounds is fine, and with Gds help, will stay that way. You're, with all due respect, no spring chicken, there's still time for you to have a wife and a family, the whole catastrophe.

Why have we never said this before? We've never seen you like this before. Sure, you *liked* Shani, a ton, she never threw you off balance. And she was the only one who lasted at all.

Rachel? She blows into your life after twenty years, now we all get it. Point is, Reuven, we've come to realize you need our help, and we want to help. You do what you need to do, *we've got this.*

Thanks for backing me up, gang, good session. For the newer baristas, I'll do a real Q and A tomorrow during lunch break. Back to work and life, everyone, we've got people to serve.

Published Minutes, Cabinet Election Update Meeting

Tuesday afternoon, 8 Iyyar, 5808, April 21, 2048, first year of the reign of His New Majesty, Hazoniyah, 24th year after the advent of His Late Majesty, the anointed one of all Israel, our Messiah, King Sar Shalom, may he rest in peace.

Jointly recorded by Tamara Nahat, interim secretary headed to HNM's communications office, training Shani Feinbaum, incoming recording secretary.

This meeting was properly calendared with the decision to hold elections, and should therefore have followed regular protocol. After HNM's call to order, however, members of His Late Majesty's advisory team requested a switch to emergency session, for a freer back and forth, dispensing with some formalities of address and respect His Old Majesty instituted.

[Recording secretaries' disclaimer: We have redacted these notes, to avoid identifying features, except where specifically noted. The attendees all agreed to hide who said what, to maximize the freedom of thought and comfort in throwing out wild ideas. To help, we have fabricated unimportant snippets, imposing a coherent flow not necessarily there at the time. We affirm, with the legal power of affidavit, we have not altered any fundamental content, and have received the approval of several attendees.

The unchanged and complete notes are on deposit in the National Archives, will be released to the public three years after the passing of the last-to-pass attendee – may Gd grant them all full lives – or upon all surviving ones choosing to waive their privacy rights.

For clarity and ease of comprehension, we have designated speakers by their being part of His Late Majesty's Cabinet, marked OG (Old Guard), or

His New Majesty's friends and advisers, marked NG (New Guard). All further inquiries about this transcript should go to His New Majesty's communications office, Tamara Nahat, incoming director.]

NG: Your Majesty, Light of Israel, Newest Anointed One –

HNM: NG, We have granted OG's request to treat this as an xtraordinary session, specifically to allow a more informal discussion. Please allow Us to say this only this once.

NG (blushes): Yes, Your Majesty, thank you. I believe my peers in NG agree with me in thanking Your Majesty for bringing us on board, putting us in an awkward position right now. We know we advocated for this election; we are chagrined over the direction it has taken, admit, with shame and regret, we were wrong to recommend it.

[OG breaks in, NG protests, His Majesty holds up a hand, gestures to NG to finish].

NG: We feared our fellow citizens would not live up to the confidence we had placed in the soundness of their judgment, watched in dismay as first signs of failure poked through. Until now, there were too many options to be sure, still time for cream to rise to the top, salvage a Knesset worthy of the name. By this point, we have reviewed the 1200 candidates for Knesset, and cannot escape the conclusion disaster looms.

HNM: Disaster? We have been rather pleased with reports so far. People appear excited, engaged, satisfied, at all levels. Polling shows the public, ordinary people, happy with their Ten-Thousand reps, despite how little input they had.

NG: Yes, Your Majesty, but with all due respect to our People Israel, they are not quite as different from other nations as they and we would hope. Like all peoples, they are often unable to spot their best interests, prone to choosing the smoothest person, ignore what really matters.

By our count, 970 of the reps have zero experience in politics, defined as broadly as we could imagine, including serving on the board of a local nonprofit. We can be sure twenty-two members of the new Knesset will fall into this category, as all the candidates for their region do. In another fourteen districts, the odds are 4:1. Yes, I am done, although I'd have appreciated more patience.

OG: I know Your Majesty has allowed us to ignore formalities, and I don't mean to make a whole introduction, but before I disagree vigorously, vehemently, and vociferously with NG, I want to make clear I respect and am deeply grateful for the long years of service and friendship the NG around this table have given Your New Majesty. Especially since most of us accepted His Late Majesty's mortality only a moment after his passing, NG members cannot be accused of opportunism; we firmly believe they worked with you all those years with no goal other than friendship and a desire for public service.

We say that to be clear we think only the best of NG, however wrong they are right now.

HNM: A worthy point, OG, but this meeting must proceed as expeditiously as possible. Those of you who helped Our father through his years will find Our surprise naive, but We confess We find the throne more of an adjustment than we expected. We still do not find enough hours in the day to properly serve Gd's people Israel. We have much to do, much to learn. Much as we value the election, we have a country to run as well; speed is of the essence, and Our time for this meeting grows short.

Let us all stipulate, by a nodding of heads and raising of hands, we all value, laud, praise, whatever word you prefer, the efforts, sincerity, and commitment of each person here, however they came to this table. Show of hands? So moved. Very well, OG, continue.

OG: We acknowledge we were skeptics. We have been doubly astonished, therefore, by how the Week has unfolded, a week *we* believe has *more* than fulfilled NG's highest hopes. True, many of the 1200 lack *political* experience. Still, they are remarkable each in their own way, philanthropists, entrepreneurs – financial and social – tech whizzes, merchandisers, teachers, religious leaders, the warp and the weft, His Late Majesty enjoyed quoting one of his late teachers, of what vaulted our country to the top of the economic and happiness indices.

Sure, these new leaders will have a learning curve, as HNM has said about himself. In their own way, they are like HNM, people who know how to learn, who are ready to adapt and flow with their new responsibilities. We see them as the best evidence of the brilliance of NG's idea, because none of them would have considered running for office in the usual system.

What person of their accomplishments would subject her or himself to the circus you see in the world's democracies? Ditto for speaking in the banalities necessary to whip up large crowds; are the people willing to do that in the name of power the kind HNM wants advising him on the people's behalf?

We recall how fond His Late Majesty was of saying, anyone willing to debase him or herself to curry favor with the rich and the mob might by that very fact disqualify themselves, how hard and often he himself had to bite down to run for office.

Indeed, perhaps HNM can confirm what has always seemed true to us, His Late Majesty remained unsure about his own political career, wondered until his last days whether he had been supposed to battle the system from the outset, instead of banking on changing it from within.

NG: Props to OG for the diligence with which they attempt to turn a weakness into a strength. The Ten-Thousand reps are an accomplished bunch, we agree, but the charm they use makes them no better as representatives than the kind who sway large crowds. Why are we preferring being good in small rooms to being good with crowds? Government takes patient negotiation and goodwill, the ability to bind together different outlooks, make the compromises His Late Majesty excelled at forging.

[A member of OG made a snide comment about NG we need not repeat here, NG responded, HNM restored order, and warned all parties to play nice.]

NG [continues]: People give charity to the causes they find interesting or worthwhile; entrepreneurs find a business or a cause they think will go somewhere, a constituency they would like to help, work with the people who agree with them.

[NG sits back, satisfied, as if their point had been made.]

OG: And? Do we not know this?

HNM: NG, allow me. Ladies and gentlemen, we have reached our stopping point, for now. Both sides have raised issues worthy of further attention. For now, We prefer to avoid any impression We wish to derail a process We started. We would lose all We gained and more should the people or any subset of them be able to claim we had decided to impose Ourselves and Our will. The elections go forward.

Forewarned is forearmed, however. We ask and urge you all to keep NG's concerns at your minds' forefront as tomorrow's results come in, to think of how to take the people as they are, work with them as we can, and think of the ways to advance us the next stone on our path.

In this room as well. Our father taught we must all work with those who do not share our views, with good will on all sides. We pray the Almighty grant us health and length of life to debate these important questions, as friends and colleagues, for weeks and decades to come.

We *must* start by insisting we are teammates – to each other and the voices in our heads – no matter how vigorously and broadly we disagree. This Throne has no doubt about the patriotism, commitment, and concern of each person around this table. We urge you all to let this fundamental truth percolate inside of you, win, lose, or draw, we seek the same outcome.

Moving on to more ordinary business...

Personal Diary of Rachel Tucker, Recorded Wednesday April 22, 2048

[Grudging permission secured from Ms. Tucker. Transcription by Media Associates, Inc. – GR]

[The recording starts with an aside, in a different tone than the entry, as follows: Israeli censors, in case you've decided to listen to this as part of some background check for projects His New Majesty may have honored me by asking me to join, I promise I'll insert the required other ways of identifying the date later, I just don't have them on the tip of my tongue. I'm working on it, I still do think in American calendar dates, sorry, and I didn't want to lose these thoughts while I looked up whatever year it is since His Late Majesty inaugurated the Third Commonwealth. Thanks, Rachel]

I thought I was going nuts, until I figured it out, it's been twenty years without a first date I had any hint might go anywhere. Longer than that if you leave my last dance with Reuven out of it. Before Reuven, I guess it'd have to be the guy who Lije, he should rest in peace, insisted I date twice, to be sure I wasn't rushing in thoughtlessly to us. Oh, Lije.

I didn't have any jitters with that guy, I didn't care what he thought of me, I was getting it out of the way as fast as possible, before Lije found someone really great. Just like all the guys after Reuven, who could never compete with a growing Jack for my main commitment.

Twenty years is definitely enough to feel like a first date. Yes, I know, conscience, I'm distracting myself to fill the twenty minutes until we'll finally be *on* the date, when I'll be too busy trying not to make a fool of myself to think of all the ways it can go wrong. Ok; as HNM seems fond of saying, forewarned is forearmed, I'm collecting conversation topics and good lines or stories.

Sure, we haven't had any trouble making conversation or being silent as we've crisscrossed this country – 57th smallest, I looked it up, and only because of the rash of microstates popping up, what with each ethnicity in the world deciding it needs its own home.

Thing is, work stops my nerves, talking about the job is a security blanket if conversation runs out. What if he's been helping me for old times' sake, or because it's good for the kingdom, or because HNM asked, tonight's his way to make sure I understand he never plans for it to go any farther? What if he cares about my middle-aged ten and new wrinkles?

Focus, Rachel, conversation topics and snippets. Ok. Reuven, which has been the most surprising Knesset race to you so far? Too business-y? Except I talk politics all the time, who wouldn't, isn't it what runs our lives? He wants to know me, this is me. Maybe I'll suggest we do a second date at that Knesset meet and greet this weekend, I bet he could get me tickets. Thirty-seven seasoned politicians welcoming newbies, forced to treat them as colleagues and equals? Who *wouldn't* want to be a fly on the wall there?

Or we could discuss Jack, I suppose, how I handled twenty years of mothering, attentive but not overbearing, as the woman said at his Health and Human Services' exit interview when he turned eighteen. What would Reuven want to know about Jack? Doesn't matter, Jack I can talk about like the back of my hand, just have to make sure I don't prattle, don't pull up videos or photos without a specific request. Fill the time, I guarantee that.

Or maybe, I suppose, I could let it ride, see where it went. Not my comfort zone, I grant you. It's why I'm offloading my nerves into you, diary, if I talk myself into exhaustion now, I have a shot at talking an appropriate amount with Reuven.

There's the bell. Coming! See you on the other side, diary, plenty of time to catch you up on the way to the journalists' part of the Knesset Committee Chair Selection retreat. Shirley *did* point out we were paying Reuven to drive me there, why was I taking my own car? I told her, the day after a date did not seem the best time to throw us together for hours. Besides, *he* doesn't need to arrive as early as I plan, scout the place for where I can corner Knesset members, catch their real thoughts on camera. He can use the time to catch up at the Grounds.

Close diary.

[Editor's Note: For those of you wondering why this is the first excerpt from a text which obviously sheds light on our story: she refused to grant me access, something about private thoughts not being anyone's business. In this one case, she had sent it to Shirley Beattie, it came out in that big ABC hack. I did need her permission, with the various laws. She was resigned, said there was no point in objecting, it's all out there somewhere anyway. You're welcome.]

Judy Mackay's Welcome to Knesset Meet, Greet, and Cabinet Selection Weekend

Welcome, Knesset members! Yes, for sure, give yourselves a round of applause, good idea, well done, all of you! My name is Judy Mackay, I'm from Kintyre, in Scotland, yes, that's right, Sir Paul did immortalize the Mull near me wee home, very good, I take it you're hoping to be on the Foreign Affairs Committee? Ha, ha.

Oh, no, how a good Scot came to be social director for corporate gatherings in Jerusalem is way too long a story for now. We'll get to it over Shabbat, if we have down time or awkward pregnant pauses. Which we definitely won't, obviously, because it's my job to fill your time enjoyably and productively!

Well, thank you, it has taken me a few years to learn how to pronounce Shabbat, I'm pleased I'm making progress. Sweet of you to notice!

Anywhooo, my staff and I will be your guides through this weekend. No, obviously, not for the religious services or Torah study sessions, your – how do I say this Sahn-head-rin? Yes? All right, well done, me! – your Sanhedrin leaders have taken care of that side. We in Group Dynamics Associates create opportunities to help you learn about each other for any purpose you all name. In this case, to choose a Cabinet, help sort yourselves into committees and chairs.

True, you *have* all spent the week winning your rooms within a few hours. HNM felt the country deserved a higher level of confidence in the candidates at this point, given the challenge of the jobs they'll be assuming. With no disrespect to any of you, who are all free to lobby to be included in the triumvirate election.

Trust us, we do this three hundred days a year, running seminars for masters of the universe, if you'll pardon the expression. Yes, business *is* booming, thank you very much, because we're excellent at it, and our best success here this weekend will be if you walk away convinced we helped you find those most poised to speak the truths power is ready to accept.

Yes, good point, thank you, Ms. – just tap your handhelds when called on, they're wired to hologram your name for all of us, help us learn each other's names – oh, *Mrs.* Gelamet, very nice, traditional family values candidate, I take it? Well, when the Palace put the idea out for bids, we pointed out how small Israel is, really. What are you, twelve million and a bit?

Barely thirty-third percentile, by population. Ok, yes, by density, you do pack it in, what are you, top twenty? Helps my point, gives the feel of a much smaller, much closer country. It's probably maximum of four degrees of separation here, right? Everybody knows everybody or knows someone who knows someone.

In such a small country, with the system His New Majesty set up, you all need to pivot. Until now, your job's been to show small groups why you're the best person to represent ten of them. Yes, yes, I know, all told you only have to deal with a little over fifty people, because each of them represents a bunch of people, and so on. I know, I know, same difference, you'll see.

Part of how I sold the Palace, we Scots know a thing or two about clans, have a bit longer history of learning to csre for the clan *and* the country. We're all here to expand our horizons without losing sight of the people we care aboot. Nope, I'm not being polite by saying we, my staff and I learn from each seminar, equips us better for the next one. Each group shows us new ways to coalesce, broadens our horizons on how many ways cooperation can look.

Other bidders went the more well-traveled route, tried to convince HNM and his staff *they* could show you the best way to sort yourselves into groups of ten, each group to pick one member of the Cabinet, one or two committee chairs.

We almost did the same. Except we realized we needed to stand out, if we'd have any success trying to take a contract away from Israeli competitors! Our desperation idea was what HNM singled out about our proposal, our goal of helping you all, together, pick the twelve, because the Cabinet must each of them and all of them together, represent this whole Knesset. At the national level, you have to pull unity out of the diversity.

After evening services, at the first meal, we'll give a more detailed description of how. Ice-breakers of course, don't roll your eyes, we do it better and more enjoyably, I promise, look up our site, you'll see plenty of sheepish gratitude in our testimonials, people more sure than you it would be cheesy and annoying, their amazement when it was fun.

Personality sharing, yep, random walks of greeting, absolutely, I know it sounds like it's the usual kitschy and awkward stuff, I'm going to have to ask you to trust me for now. Or trust we couldn't possibly snow HNM and his advisers. Of course, interspersed will be lectures, breakout sessions, group study, volunteering trips, as the Sanhedrin leaders requested.

Right now, look around. Left, right, diagonally, see if you can make eye contact, for a second, with each of your fellow members. These are your *colleagues*. Let each face become memorable and important. You've spent a week where your job was to focus on nine to nineteen other people. Now? All 120 of you need to learn to work with every other person here, knowing you'll disagree, deeply, angrily, people will push your buttons, unwittingly or maliciously. Some of you will speak in ways you shouldn't.

All part of the puzzle, why we start by taking a moment now to try to remember we're all doing our best for the country we love. No need to be nervous, we'll do this. Together. Take a deep breath, let it out. Another.

Here's the pivot you have to make, and quickly: You earned your place here through your listening and collation skills, your ability to reflect back what your fellow reps said, respecting everyone's views, let everyone feel heard, cared about and included in the eventual decision for how to meet as many people's needs as possible.

Do that now, you'll pick great Million-reps, where Israel needs a Cabinet, ministers responsible for one area of our public needs, foreign relations, housing, commerce, something, who can also oversee complex institutions, have the skills to shepherd government workers into working smoothly and well.

What are those skills? Not my job to say, it's my job to frame the problem in a way you find stimulates you to the answer you believe to be true. Along with my wonderful staff, Calum, Camdyn, Lachlan, Leith, Cullodena,

Kirsty, Kyla, and Skye, yes, a round of applause is more than welcome, thanks, they're all vital to our success.

The first ice breaker, after ...ooh, boyo, you people like this sound, me Scottish Gaelic's rusty, as are me gutturals, so it's what, Mincha? Yes? Score! After...that prayer, we'll all share a formative incident in our lives, or the words someone said to us at a key point.

I'll start, give you a sense of what works best. You won't usually have this much time to prepare, we're hoping you can each be brief, and we all know that does take preparation. Be sure to prepare enough to be able to pay attention to each other, because after we go around the small groups, we'll *re*-group you, ask you to share something touching or moving someone *else* from your original group said. Oh, don't groan, you'll see, it'll be fun, and funny. As long as you're all as personable as winning Hundred-Thousand rep rooms means you should be.

Last point: remember the Cabinet will also choose the candidates for Prime Minister, Chief Technical Officer, and Minister of Public Relations/ Foreign Affairs. Also – ok, it wasn't my last point, I'm terrible at endings – I want to introduce Reuven HaOzer. Whom, from the sound of it, apparently many of you know, all right, my job just got a little easier. Reuven has learned a thing or two about helping people open up in his years at his coffeeshop, what was it called, yes, The Temple Grounds. Oh, I get it, hahaha, that's funny!

Anyway, Shani Feinbaum suggested him to liaise between my team and the Sanhedrin, help us not step on any religious toes. HNM has also asked him to help however else he sees fit. If he asks you a question, trust me, he's not looking to trip you up, he's looking to show a productive place to share, because the sooner and better you know each other, the more informed a decision you can make. Tends to work out well for everyone.

Last point for real this time, meet Rachel Tucker, some of you know her, I don't want anyone to misunderstand what she's doing here. All events, conversations, and interactions *are completely off the record*, for a minimum of fifteen years, unless they're criminal, ha, ha, not that they would be.

Rachel is a journalist, true, and she *will* record her impressions, we are telling you ahead of time there will be no names or identifying details – and we don't mean she'll use your middle name, as if no one can think of looking that up, we mean *no identifying details*. There are also cameras basically everywhere, again sealed for fifteen years, then evaluated for release.

Don't be *too* relaxed, in other words. Be open, be yourselves, but your best selves. I'm sorry, what? Oh, wow, thank you! Ladies and gentlemen, a surprise and an honor, His New Majesty Hazoniyah will offer words of greeting and then join us for Min – the upcoming services.

Members of the Incoming Knesset of 2048, welcome! On behalf of Our palace staff, Our Inner Circle, Old Guard and New, We wanted to be sure to express good wishes and excitement about the work we will do together. Far as you all have come, this weekend promises to tax your clearly formidable talents. The eyes of Israel are upon you, hoping you make choices of clear wisdom.

Perception matters, We remind all of you, and hope you bring us a government the people will immediately respect and applaud. We wish you well, beseech Our Father in Heaven to send you the insight to identify what we all need in these untrodden times. Best wishes for a peaceful, fulfilling Shabbat. Mr. HaOzer? Mincha, yes? Has anyone else here lost a relative in the past month? No? Then I shall lead. *Ashrei…*

Whistleblower Complaint and Memo

To: Marcia Wasperson, Ombudsperson, ABC New/Entertainment

Cc: Buffy Dachs, Ombudsperson, Walt Disney Companies., Jenny Kelter, Ombudsperson, ABC Worldwide

From: Rachel Tucker

Re: ABC Special Event, "What the New Israeli Cabinet Means for You"

Note: Whistleblower protocol invoked, however far it extends

My legal counsel insists I explicitly acknowledge she warned me against filing this. She has given me sound legal advice, telling me I may not qualify as a whistleblower because of my personal and financial stake in the incident I am reporting.

I acknowledge she has done her duty in making me aware the courts have not yet been clear as to the legality of corporate retaliation for an employee cloaking personal grievances as whistleblower revelations. I hereby absolve her of any repercussions I may suffer, immunize her from any malpractice lawsuits.

I proceed anyway, certainly because I have been hurt, as has been my security at ABC News, my confidence I will be able to stay in this job for the length of my contract; I've never pretended to be dispassionate or objective, my passion has always anchored my reporting. I believe it's also always helped me connect with sources and audiences, including the new one ABC has trumpeted my finding.

I also believe ABC News will suffer if I am ignored, why I hope you ombudspersons will pay attention, regardless of legal necessity. I have twenty-seven years invested in this network's future, watching you guys shoot yourselves in the foot bothers me, my own issues aside.

To the matter, the promiscuous spread of information I procured and shared with others at ABC for internal use only. For context, the same supervisor who aired "What the New Cabinet in Israel Means for You" over my protests and before I had a chance to appeal, has now put me on notice for sub-par performance, accused me of failing to meet quota.

Look, I've seen the ratings and revenue numbers, I know one hour of that show recouped the costs of the whole death/funeral/election, I get it, had I been an exec, I'd have been tempted, too. Break-even on a foreign affairs story? Fuhgeddaboutit, I know.

Grabbing the gold ring is still sometimes short-sighted. The story had tidbits shared with me as deep background – clearly marked as such in my reports – not for publication until I could find a source willing to go on or off the record. *Could* we have found people the new Cabinet members helped with life crises, or convinced some of the Cabinet to take credit other people were telling us they deserved? Would members of the teen gangs for whom a Cabinet member brokered peace at home and in four foreign countries have gone on the record if we pushed?

I assume, but we *didn't* push (nor did anyone suggest I spend the time and resources any of those option would have taken). Now the people who clued me in are at risk of being shut out of the information game. Who wants to be kicked to the curb, with all to show for it having helped someone soon to be dismissed at ABC for lowered productivity?

Say these people do salvage their careers, *my* access to them is over, barring some miraculous repair of our rupture. Next time I want a story, next time they have info they're thinking of sharing with the media-verse, they're going to say, "Rachel Tucker? Nu-*uhhh,* she'll use deep background material on air."

To anticipate the CYA question, no, we had no written agreement, we didn't *technically* violate anything, that's not how this works, you know that.

I'm most frustrated by the stupidity. We were so far ahead of any other network in the Explain Israel to America space, we didn't *need* a home run, we could have made our money the old-fashioned way, steady good stories, no prize winners. Because yes, you guys forcing me here made me the first foreign reporter, gave me a big stake in staying beyond the funeral.

And then, it worked out better than we'd hoped. The Palace took a shine to me, thanks to Reuven, I have had hints of some sort of formal arrangement, again thanks to Reuven. (I include his role to remind you of the grief HQ gave me about his extra cost. The nickel and diming is for another memo.)

Now, we at ABC News might have blown all of it. Next time someone at Palace media says, "we're thinking of Rachel Tucker and ABC News," Cabinet staff, friends, advisers, or janitors – whoever my sources were – are going to veto, in the kind of whisper we cannot address or rebut. "Rachel Tucker, are you kidding? You can't trust her!"

I know the ombuds process calls for you to question the sources I am claiming are upset at being outed. Can't be done, this person or people *cannot* be seen with us, it would confirm his/her/their role. Besides, you have all you need, me on tape, aired for all the world, crowing over how many future Cabinet members I predicted. Predictions I made thanks to *classified sources*, let's say it together one last time, to whom I promised full and effective cover.

Maybe you don't care, you think you can make it up to the Palace and Cabinet without me, you'll be free of my "albatross of a contract," as I know one supervisor likes to gripe.

Except, remember Reuven. He's still on our payroll, doing his job, yes, but. After the fiasco – *he* connected me to the source or sources involved – he's receded to the letter of his agreement, knocks off at five every day to check his stores, has slowed his story ideas to a faucet dribble, where he used to be an ever-replenishing gusher of a fountain.

All well within the terms of his contract, he had a kick-butt lawyer. You don't realize what you had until it's… well, you know. I've seen the dailies, the ratings are suffering, and people give a bit of slack before they go away forever. We can recover only by addressing it, forthrightly and contritely. *Sincerely* contritely.

To whatever intern is reading this (I'm not naive), I hope you're not thinking of dismissing me as another woman upset about the end of a relationship. Whatever is or isn't going on with Reuven and me, however recent events affected us – none of it your business – everything I've said stands on its own. Also, my main goal in coming here, remember, wasn't Reuven, it was Jack, keeping his tuition checks flowing.

Thank you for reading, and please keep the following words in mind at whatever 3-D meeting discusses, dispenses, and disposes of this memo: Short-term thinking, long-term cost. Hard road, smart road. I know you'll say it's on me to repair relationships with sources, no matter what you nim-nulls did and do. I'm working on it, an ounce of prevention would have done wonders here; after the fact, we need to actively recommit to our professionalism, in a way convincing to my sources.

Heads need to roll, and not mine.

Reuters/AP/UPI News Flash: Making the News, Not Breaking It: ABC Falls Into Dreaded Pit

Two surprising developments at ABC News/Entertainment today. Ryan Williamson, rumored to be a lock for joining the exec team at ABC World, the parent company, has resigned to find more family-time-friendly opportunities. He has opened a media consultancy and will teach a course at Columbia's Journalism School.

Williamson's press agent returned our calls on his behalf. Quaisha Federson told us Mr. Williamson wants to convey how much he enjoyed his time at ABC, the gratitude he will always feel for the training he received, the successes he was given room to find, and will cherish the many relationships he built there.

"With his youngest children approaching the end of high school, Mr. Williamson decided this was his last time to focus on them."

He and his family have taken a seven news cycles' vacation, the spokesperson said, to recharge, reboot, and refresh.

Company spokespeople insist their second announcement is unrelated. ABC News today issued an unusually full-throated apology for mishandling a recent story.

"'Despite the thirty million views we received for 'What the New Cabinet Means for You,' it was our error in airing the show. Informative and well-researched as it was, internal miscommunications led us to breach the confidence of sources who spoke on deep background. Our investigation will wind its slow way to the truth; in the meantime, we wish to make clear the story went forward with neither the help nor consent of Rachel Tucker, the reporter entrusted with the information improperly included. ABC regrets the error."

We at Reuters/AP/UPI would never gloat, and wish to be extra careful to avoid the appearance of gloating. Still, we quote journalism scholar Maya Brittany Evers:

"Admitting wrongdoing has been out of fashion for decades. Hold your ground, deny all, push ahead, has been the motto across the industry for generations of newspersons. It's a great move by ABC, suggests we might be entering an exciting era, when propriety again becomes a concern, competitive with covering our behinds."

Reuters/AP/UPI's many connections to ABC News/Entertainment, friendly, cooperative, and competitive, mean we could not possibly say more with any objectivity. Inquiring minds will nonetheless inevitably wonder what brought this sea change.

Does Rachel Tucker have something on her higher-ups? We could not reach her for comment; our reporter did catch her entering a famed Jerusalem eatery, The Temple Grounds.

Instead of answering his questions, she said, tears in her eyes, "Can you leave me alone for a bit of a private life? Haven't these stories cost me enough?"

Interesting times at ABC, the kind from Chinese curses.

Closing-Time Summary, The Temple Grounds

Staff Member Overseeing Closing: Reuven

Hey gang, I know I've been a bit AWOL recently, it's why I grabbed the opportunity to take the late shift, give y'all a chance to get home early for a change. Not much happened, we had good contributions from our temporary/trainee baristas, Corinna, Darlene, Xander and Yaron, we thank them for all their hard work and look forward to having them on-board full-time when they complete the coursework and hours.

I've put the supplies list in the joint doc, orders will be placed tomorrow. Going forward, please keep an eye out on our milk levels, we've had a surge in people ordering just milk to go with their biscotti or muffins. Not hot milk, either, be sure not to mess up a milk by heating it and then have to throw it out. But also, it means we have to be more on top of our supplies, it would be bad if we ran out of milk, right?

For those of you who prepare based on the previous day, today was less about personal problems, people wanted to share the experience of the campaign. It felt like – just me talking, take it with the grain of salt it deserves – they haven't had a political campaign in so long, they want to enjoy it with other people. If you don't have family or friends, or your family and friends aren't as invested in the country's future as you are, or we at The Temple Grounds *are* your family or friends, well, you were there with us tonight.

I'm not one of those, would have watched the debates alone were I not on duty, but I gotta tell you, it was kinda fun. The kibitzing and catcalls stayed good-natured, thank Gd, even though it turned out different candidates had different kinds and levels of support. I would not have thought our little store would draw in such a diverse set of views. I *was* proud, and I hope we can keep it up, of how civilly people disagreed *and debated*. Great conversations, on real topics, with lots of ideas for how to move forward, not one time did I have to step in to ask people to tone it down or leave out the ad hominem. A credit to all of you, for the atmosphere you've built at our little shop, the norms we've made second nature at The Temple Grounds. I am humbled to be part of the team, and thank you all for taking my kernel and growing it beyond what I ever imagined.

A last point, a bit personal. I would apologize for mixing business with personal, except certainly The Grounds *is* my family and friends. I know many of you have noticed my divided loyalties in the past couple of weeks, I know we had issues we had to work through, in the big group settings and in the one on ones a bunch of you have had with me. I thank you all for your forthrightness, I appreciate the critics for their honesty, am grateful to those who wished me well along the way.

The outside contract I allowed myself to take on, with your collective agreement, will come to an end immediately following the election, and then I'm happy to say I'll be back 110%. We reach crossroads in life, where we think the time has come to move to new endeavors, take on new relationships, focus our energies in a new direction.

I dipped a toe in, thought it might be my time, only to realize I have more to do here.

With your permission, I'll be around for a while, happy to be part of the next stages for The Temple Grounds. We've got expansions internal and external, I have some ideas about how we can shorten our response and therapy times, streamline our referrals process.

HNM is starting new, let's do it, too. Thanks for your forbearance, and I'm glad you're all along for the ride!

The Careerist: A Blog, Candidates' Debate Edition

[Edited for concision and relevance]

7:47 pm: Pendleton Samuels here, welcome to my vlogging of tonight's debate from Jerusalem, Israel. I know how many options you have for how to enjoy this momentous evening, thank you for making me your home for tonight. The Israeli government has arranged simul-translation, you won't need me to tell you the basics; my value-added, I hope, builds on my fifteen years in the British consulates and embassies to the Court of His Majesty Sar Shalom of blessed memory (as they say in Jerusalem).

We'll do our best to help you look smart around the water cooler tomorrow morning, maybe win a few bucks in the office pool by predicting who ends up Prime Minister, who Chief Technology Officer, and who Minister for Foreign and Press Relations.

I don't want to overload you, I'll pop in only as occasion warrants, not insult your intelligence as if you cannot bear silence. See you when it gets started.

7:54 pm: Not much doing yet, as they assemble on the stage in the old Rebecca Crown/ Daphne Faigelson auditorium of the Jerusalem Theater. Interesting story, that, and since they're fumbling with mics, camera angles, and whatnot, I have a moment to share it.

When King Sar-Shalom ob"m (of blessed memory; I add the term because I wish to maintain fruitful relationships with Israelis, who care about including it as much as you all care about not having religion foisted on you. I don't mean I'm doing it only for them – I would never patronize them that way – I mean I might have kept my own sadness over the loss of Sar Shalom to myself, or expressed it more ecumenically. Hard to satisfy everybody, but

I try.)

Anyway, as I was saying, when King Sar-Shalom ob"m was rebuilding the Temple and surrounding city, he opted against using public funds, never mind he had the government in the black for the previous few years, a first sign he was the Messiah. Many of his advisers have gone on record they advocated raising funds in the time-honored fashion, selling dedications.

Who *wouldn't* sponsor the Ark of the Covenant or the Menorah in a rebuilt Temple? He could have sold them three and four times over, funded the construction and first few years of upkeep. What price wouldn't some fat cat pay?

If you like classic videos as much as I do, you know what he did next. If you don't, look it up, it's remarkable, the fireside chat where you see the horror on his face as he speaks of the possibility of dedication plaques lining the walls of Gd's House. A great quote: "Where we once had money changers, will we now err in selling the building itself?"

His choice brings us back to tonight's theater. He decided he'd re-sell dedications to every *other* public building in Jerusalem, all of Israel, if necessary. To arrange it, he approached all the original donors (or their survivors) for permission to add a name. Remember, a lot of those buildings had walls packed with names, he had to track down all the heirs, survivors, or representatives of each one.

It was a smarter move than maybe he realized, ninety percent asked him how much he needed to keep just their one name on it. The rest of course said yes, who could say no to rebuilding the Temple? That's how you're looking at a debate space/theater where Frank and Velma Faigelson chose to add his name to Rebecca Crown's, with her family's consent.

They're closing in on starting, still time for another point: tickets for tonight's debate were a *hot* item, the government could have sold out the Sherover/Antebe Theater, double the size, in addition to all the closed-circuit venues. We're told they're doing it here to keep a cozy feeling, is why you can see the crowd chatting as they file into their seats.

Last point: as you set yourselves up with chips and beer or salmon and tea, or whatever food and beverage are at the center of your game, be sure to let sink in how remarkable a choice the new king, yes, Hazoniyah is his name, thank you, Roland, off-camera producer everyone, Roland Barrington IV, King Hazoniyah, has made. A fully-functioning monarch, with close to what we Westerners would think of as despotic power, no rebellions or protests on the horizon, no pressure to yield power, has voluntarily decided to have the people choose his advisers.

All this old cynic's way of saying we're in for a treat, the chance to become familiar with the people who will lead the government of the most influential nation in the world.

8:02 pm: Whoa, right out of the gate, these three know how to make a splash! Good on them, flipping the script. They're right, the new system *does* mean they'll have to work together no matter what, does mean the country's better off seeing them interact, give voters a sense of how each speaks and works, because the question is where to slot them, not whom to elect.

They have a fine idea, a conversation, but if I were tonight's moderator – and I'm not saying I should have been, not saying I'd have jumped on a flight given half a chance – if I were Jacqueline DeParis, I'd feel blind-sided. For a job like that, I'd have spent days picking questions to elicit the most personality revealing answers, I'd have scoured my brain and the world for ways to catch them off-guard, trick or trap them into saying something they ordinarily wouldn't.

And here they go, catch me as moderator off guard. I'd be wondering why they couldn't have contacted me *ahead of time*, worked *with* me, on a new plan. Who knows, maybe they thought it would make for a more free-flowing, less scripted, back and forth.

Except if I'm her, I don't have time to wonder, I have to figure out where to go next, tout suite. Good job, candidates. Good luck, Ms. DeParis.

8:05pm: Good recovery, no, *excellent* recovery. The influence of Frenchies in today's Israel gives her the security of knowing no one would elbow her totally out of the spotlight. Not letting them get to you is the first step, having a social worker on call shows solid prep, she must have sensed these candidates were the kind to pull this kind of stunt.

It's the best of both worlds for her, she can speak up every few minutes, remind us she's still there. Me, too. As I'm sure many of you are thinking, they've thrown me the same curveball as her, my research likely won't matter, they're all playing nice. I hold out hope my years of with Israelis has given me insight you will find helpful as the night wears on.

My staff's working on factoids on the social worker, Genevieve Mizrahi, bear with me, I'm toggling screens, you'll be the first to hear. As always, and as I am contractually required to slip into conversation every five minutes, we thank No Bull Energy, Spike Athletic Gear, and pairup.com, pairing you in romance, business, and graduate school.

Need a pair or partner? Go to pairup.com.

8:17pm: I don't know about you, I'm a sucker for accomplished people who fawn over each other, the more accomplished the better, shows they haven't bought too far into the hype. Except if they were all in the *same* field, I'd say it's a required script, fake graciousness. Looks to me, and I hope you'll message me if I'm on the mark, these three are the rarer bird of honest admiration. They seem secure enough in their accomplishments not to feel the need to curry favor. That's how a town stays big enough for many big people.

8:29pm: A call for comments, and – thanks to our friends at Spike Gear – the comment with the most likes or replies earns a $100 gift card to the Spike near you: Genevieve Mizrahi allowing Lem Orantal to show his intro film for potential donors to Cool the Earth, good move, lets us all know him most efficiently, or a mistake, free publicity for him and his charity? Lots of possible answers, I'm not judging right and wrong.

But don't say, well, the other two agreed. What were they going to do, look petty?

It's a well-done video, true, and slash417@messiahland.com says it well, this isn't slick, self-promoting pap, you got to respect a guy who took on the weather instead of talking about it. My question is: will the others call out the emperor's clothes? You can bet none of them believes convincing three million people a year to spend the summer in cooler climates nudges the needle on warming. Will they challenge him to prove the heat they use to stave off the cold doesn't balance the reduction in air-conditioning?

Personally, I wish he'd told us more about his water initiative. Like, could someone please ask him *why* he's planning on investing in bringing tourists to Jerusalem for Tabernacles, what makes him think it will improve their water situation back home? A question we'll have to hope will be raised during audience participation, they're moving on to the next speaker, so, Candidate One for your scorecards and quick jotting of first impressions: Lem Orantal, social entrepreneur with a promising early stage charity, and an easy, charming manner.

8:35pm: Strong work by candidate two, Sophia Mosseri, I wouldn't have thought anyone could speak about her fifteen start-ups and thirteen board seats without sounding self-important. Think about this: she's got to be a centi-millionaire, maybe billionaire, and she's avoided the limelight well enough *I'd* never heard of her. Good for DeParis, asking how she'd transition from the under the radar role she's worked to cultivate, to these front-seat ones.

8:41pm: Ok, benefit of the doubt time, their opening statements were pretty traditional ways to open a debate, when they promised us a conversation. Let's be sure to notice the better rhythm we're hitting, they're finding better flow. Except Mizrahi keeps focusing them on feelings – sorry, I should have said Genevieve Mizrahi, the social worker, brought on stage by the moderator, Jacqueline DeParis, to facilitate the candidates' conversation. My apologies, it's a pet peeve of mine, makes it doubly bad I did it, referred to her by last name only, as if I can be sure you remember her from one previous reference.

I guess it's an occupational hazard, feelings are the coin of her realm. I want to watch them talk about how to run a government where the king can overrule you at any moment.

8:57pm: Finally, a memorable quote, thank you, Aderet Ushidi: "How can I know until I'm in there? I can tell you my *plans* for each of the offices, of course I've thought about each, it would irresponsible not to. To tell you what I'll *do*, would be misleading. Whatever office the good citizens of Israel honor me to fill, I'm going to meet the people with whom I'll be working, especially His New Majesty, long may he reign, and his staff, looking for where we can make productive progress.

"I can tell you what I'd *like* to do, my overall *direction*, but it will all depend on my colleagues. And on all of you, how you communicate to your reps which parts of what I try appeal to you and which don't.

Or, I can tell you how I *tend* to approach problems, my biggest strengths, such as convincing others to work with me, letting them know I will work for their goals, too. Anything else I say is fantasy or dreams."

Nice, an honest awareness of the limits of any leader. I like her already.

9:22pm: I know, I know, it's been almost a half an hour and I haven't written, but if you're watching the same program I am, you'd see they've left me nothing to say. These are consummate pros, impressive accomplishments with remarkable potential, already working well with and off each other.

You don't need me, is my point. I'd trust any of the three with any of the jobs. True, I have thoughts about the best slot for each, as do you, what do you gain from reading it here? Confirm what you already think? Annoy you with a different view?

Maybe the best compliment I can give them, they're transparent, no veil to pierce, leaves me literally nothing. Which I know will surprise my loyal subscribers, whom I thank for joining me today or tonight, depending where you are, as they have in the seventy-five worldwide events we have vlogged here before. As well as my sponsors, No Bull energy, for serious energy when you need it, no bull; Spike Athletic Gear, in the hopes you and your skin never SAG; and pairup.com for when you need a quick pairup.

I'll wait a couple more minutes before signing off, trust me, I'm *looking* to comment.

9:40pm: All right, I guess I'm out. I am wordless, a rare affliction. Thanks, sorry, and good night. For those who want to blame someone when life goes unexpectedly, refunds are available through my producer, Roland Barrington IV.

This has been Pendleton Samuels, failing to add much to the debate/conversation at the Crown/Faigelson Jerusalem Theater. Good night, see you next month as we vlog the expected coup in Pakistan.

GOSSIP! Alert: Trouble in Paradise?

Alert viewers, thousands of whom have the good sense to be *GOSSIP!* readers, have noticed what's missing from Rachel Tucker's broadcasts for three days now. Reuven HaOzer, fan favorite, absent, no explanation provided. Taking the show's special spark with him. Rachel's fine, and we'll watch her forever, but now we know it could be better.

GOSSIP! reached out to ABC News/Entertainment on your behalf – we take our role seriously as your representative to the world of celebrities – and received the following statement from the office of Shirley Beattie, recently promoted to Acting VP for International Broadcasts:

"Ms. Beattie thanks *GOSSIP!* and its readers for their kind good wishes on her new position. In response to your query, Reuven HaOzer remains a valuable and valued member of Rachel's team. He is also a successful small business owner, and his chain of stores, especially the Temple Grounds in the center of Jerusalem, have recently needed more of his time and presence. He continues to drive Rachel to breaking stories, and Rachel credits him as a main reason for her iron lock on the top of the ratings. Thanks for contacting ABC News!"

Look, *we* know they're blowing smoke, *GOSSIP!* readers are certainly astute enough to know they're blowing smoke. Reuven doesn't have a family to give the usual line of wanting to spend more time with them, part of the reason we've been able to enjoy the sparks with Rachel so much – it would be worse if he was abandoning a wife and kids for her, right? You always want to have known about the next happy celebrity couple before anyone else, for bragging rights at your next dinner party, we get it, we know how gossip works. It's literally our name.

The last few days seem to have killed our happy ending. *GOSSIP!* is sad to say – we rooted for them as much as anyone – in our experience, celebrities like Rachel Tucker give a relationship one try, the couple stops appearing in public, it's over, moving on. Sad, we know, the longer you do this job, the more you know chemistry like theirs doesn't come along every day. You want lovey-dovey couples, go on over to *WE!* Mag, they make it their business to catch every PDA by anyone with over a million followers on any platform.

Here at *GOSSIP!* we look for deeper connections, the snatched glances telling us a couple sees the world the same way, laughs at the same silliness of the people around them. Only then do we help you learn to care about them as a couple. It's just too hard on all of us to invest in those one or two year relationships, who has the emotional energy for that many roller coasters? Who would *want* to have the energy for that many roller coasters?

Besides, Israel's strict PDA rules means *WE!* wouldn't have caught on to Rachel and Reuven until they married. Body language, smiles, leanings-in, tilts of the head, in Israel, that's how you sense solidity. Our bad, we were sure they'd go the distance.

It's not over until it's over, but for now, it seems to be over. We'll be on the lookout for their first rebound relationship, we promise. Join us back here at *GOSSIP!* often, because news breaks fast in the world of gossip, and you want your dopamine hits as soon as they're available!

The Temple Grounds Site, Testimonials Tab

Hey, long-time customer, first-time writer. A little embarrassing, I guess, I mean, I probably *should* have written before, I've always loved the store, I *talk* about the muffins, the coffee, the atmosphere, all the time, my friends make fun of me for it, call me Temple Grounds guy. Until they go for their first time, get hooked, and the teasing stops.

I always figured, who would trust some stranger's view online? Besides, with a name as common as Moshe Levy, I assumed people would tag me for a fake account or a sockpuppet for the owners.

Today was the first time I went in with a problem big enough to pay for the hour concierge service. Nothing too terrible, I was having trouble sleeping at night, was up at 5am anyway, figured they might have an open slot, and they did. To my delight and shock, I drew Reuven HaOzer himself! He told me he's been making up for lost time, has been taking whole days at the store, 5am-9pm, paying back people who covered for him during the election.

"With the end of my broadcast career, I have to make sure the store also doesn't kick me to the curb, you know?" he said with a smile.

I'm telling you, if I'd known I was going to get him, I'd have booked two hours, that's not how it works, you know, they don't want people fixating on a therapist, they want people working through their problems with an attentive listener offering bits of advice. Or else go the more formal therapy route.

Thank God, I won't need it, Reuven set me straight pretty quickly and pretty effectively. He let me ramble on for almost as long as I wanted, and naming my anxieties always gives me relief. A less experienced guy might have stopped there, let me leave, then I'd have been stuck when they came rushing back later in the day. Might have blamed myself for backsliding.

He's too much of a pro. He listened almost wordlessly. Fourth time I came around the same circle, he breaks in to ask if he might summarize what he thinks he's heard. I shrug, he starts, and he's gotten me totally, puts everything I said into a way prettier package than I'd have come up with. My basic problem, he asks, is the future, right?

I hadn't said that, hadn't known it until he said the words. With the nudge, I realized, "yeah, and it's because of His Late Majesty, how many years I spent waking up in the morning, with no worry about the future. I could live my life, make my plans, roll with the punches as they came, because I knew it could never get too far off track. Then, he passes, boom, anxiety."

Reuven smiled at me, gentlest, sweetest, most understanding smile I could imagine. I'd have thought he was having problems with the future, too, except he's Reuven HaOzer, you know, what problems does he have?

Then, *he* says to me – *me,* a walk-in he's never served before – "I also just recently found out the future wasn't going to go as I'd hoped. Knocked me for a loop, too. It's rough, no doubt."

Five minutes, I watched the clock, five minutes we sat in silence, sharing our insecurity about the future. I broke first. "What do we do about it?"

He shrugged. "What we can, and leave the rest to our Father in Heaven. Whose salvation comes *ke-heref ayin,* blink of an eye. Or, as they say in the States, you gotta believe!"

I know lots of believers, people who find the weirdest gurus, oddest spiritual guides, decide to accept all the wild stuff they say. Had you told me Reuven would show me another kind of belief, where a bit of a nudge comes at the right time, I'd have snickered.

He did it anyway. I'm waiting for the *heref ayin,* the blink of Gd's eye, the next step in this crazy ride we've been on since Our Late Messiah arrived and now has passed. Go to the Temple Grounds, anyone who reads this, find faith, find security, find comfort.

Israel National News Broadcast

[Ok, this is a bit touchy, my apologies ahead of time. I wanted to post the video, told my publisher a multisensory experience enhances reading. He snorted – literally snorted, and I mean literally literally, not figuratively literally – said anyone interested in mixed media wouldn't be reading books, they'd read articles, those already come with other formats interspersed.

No knock against the publisher, I don't know his business, we compromised, I'm going to share my best description of the video. I hope it comes across in the sharing – GR]

The shot opens in the streets outside the Palace, the same streets where Rachel Tucker stood a few weeks before, interviewing those lined up for a condolence call to the Royal Family. The fences for the pens are long gone, the only barriers to entry are the gates where two security guards check ID. You might think it's insecure, a truck could easily ram through and hit the Palace before anyone could stop it. You're forgetting the force field, adept enough to neutralize a large-scale attack, the machines were for small weapons people might bring in.

Which I mention because in the video, the streets are filled with people dancing, singing, hugging, shouting, and the security guards are calm, look like they wish they could join in. Security experts to whom I've shown it are outraged, say if they were on duty, a crowd is always a worry, a shooter might hide within until the last second. These guys aren't like that at all.

The singing and shouting are in Hebrew, the usual songs of Israeli celebration, Hava Nagila (Let's Rejoice) and Am Yisrael Hai (The Jewish Nation Lives), classics from the early days of the original State, along with more recent entries like *Agila ve-Esmeha* (I Will Rejoice and Be Happy) and *Sal'I u-Metzudati* (The Lord is My Rock and Fortress), and then, slowly taking over the entire crowd, an old song with new words *Hazoniyah, Melekh Yisrael*

(Hazoniyah – the new king – King of Israel; the rest of the words are *hai vekayyam,* should live forever).

Three or four minutes into the video, an impromptu stage pops up, a bunch of late middle-aged men and women – seventies, just experienced enough to begin to command respect by virtue of their age – are pushed forward, they climb up, a hush happens. Seven speeches follow, polished, articulate, mix content with humor and anecdotes, eye contact, each has a personal twist, you never feel they're reading off the same cookie cutter manual.

They did agree a bit too much, made the speeches a bit repetitive. I'll share the translation only of the first:

"The Lord is our Shepherd, we shall not want. The passing of a revolutionary leader has always been difficult for our nation – successors for the Vilna Gaon, the seventh Lubavitcher Rebbe, the Breslover Rebbe, Rabbi Joseph B. Soloveitchik, took years or decades to emerge. Our Late Majesty Sar Shalom, too, left a hole in our lives we had not been certain could be filled.

His New Majesty has refused to claim he is equal to the task. His commendable humility, at the meetings I was invited to attend, have led him to be clear our only salvation will be when the Lord chooses to send it. Until then, he has been saying, we will need to muddle along, do our best, trust if we do our part, the Lord will do His.

Way deep down, if we are honest, who of us believed our prayers would come to fruition this quickly? My friends and I, all rabbis, all treated with the respect due elders of the Jewish people, all able to infer valid new ideas from the ones presented us, all knowledgeable, thought we would have to wait perhaps a generation or two, for the next revolutionary leader, for the descendant of His Late Majesty who knew how to follow him in breaking paradigms, could guide us in a brilliant new direction.

Today's announcement, and I remind you of the Palace's request to maintain its secrecy, to keep all details away from non-residents of Israel, tells us the spirit of the Lord that resided in the father continues in the son. Heaven showed His Late Majesty the force field, solving our military, financial, and political problems, started us on the road to realizing he was our long-awaited Messiah.

The outside world? They'd have dismissed it as a *deus ex machina,* the kind of trick some novelist comes up with because she can't figure out how to move the plot. We knew then and know now, that's how salvation comes. We do ours, reach the end of the road, Hashem takes us the rest of the way. Twenty years later, we still reap the benefits.

Today, HNM has shown he, too, merited the hand of Hashem in giving us the next giant leap forward for the community of the Jewish people, and it heralds a bright future indeed. Yes, brethren, sing, dance, and praise Gd, Who has sent us a son worthy of succession, a son we can truly call Messiah!"

[I know you think I've left out the key part, where they described whatever HNM had done. I haven't. Each speaker referred to *something* remarkable, none gave hints to what it could be. I did research it, found pretty good clues, and I have reproduced them in the coming chapters.

One more aspect of the video bears stressing before we move on. These people are *raucously* joyous, celebrating something they didn't see coming, didn't imagine, maybe couldn't have imagined as a *possibility*. They already lived free of our worries, already would have told us they were living in the halcyon Messianic days. The way they react here, it's like *now* the future is solved.

Bliss, that's the word I'm looking for, HNM has given this people bliss, and they were celebrating appropriately. It might take us outsiders another twenty years to fully understand it. Meanwhile, the video's available for those who want to check up on me, contact my publisher for the link. Or search it, it's not that hard to find. – GR]

CoSIP Patent Application, Israel 48-3002

Duly filed this day, 5 May, 2048, with the Court of Secret International Patents (CoSIP), Oslo, Norway.

Filing Official: Sophia Mosseri, Chief Technology Officer, Court of His New Majesty Hazoniyah, State of Israel.

Patent Examiner: Oleg Svendjarfssen, Senior Patent Attache.

Per court procedures, the device has been fully described orally to the Examiner, partially demonstrated, descriptions and demonstration omitted from this document for security reasons. This report establishes presumption, shifts the burden of proof to anyone suing to challenge the patent herein granted, seeks to patent a similar device, or any device with similar uses.

Pursuant to any lawsuit proceeding to the discovery phase, the CoSIP court retains the right to break the seal on the more complete documentation provided by the Israelis.

Description of Device and Purpose: CTO Mosseri spoke of a team who discovered the device, without telling us how many people shared the initial insight, who or how many were involved in building a working model, or any other details of the process, any bumps on the road from theory to practice. We cannot imagine more than one person would have decided, out of the blue, the world has invisible connections unrecognized by science.

Whoever had the intellectual daring to speculate there were aspects of this world left to be discovered would seem likely to be the one also willing to indulge such a crazy idea as to link those connections to place names, although our time at this court has shown us many people with one brilliant insight who fail to see the next step. CTO Mosseri did say they had yet to figure out how or why their device worked, they have gotten as far as a way to travel along the links – and not yet all of them, as we will see.

Readers will likely assume I mean teleportation, a word Ms. Mosseri rejected more sharply than applicants usually allow themselves when speaking with the man who controls their financial future.

"Mr. Svendjarfssen, the moment you meet a working teleportation machine, booth, ship, or whatever, you give the person who shows it to you a patent in perpetuity as far as we are concerned, and more power to them. We worked on teleportation for years, under His Late Majesty Sar Shalom, he was sure there had to be a way to make the combustion engine obsolete. Made not a lick of progress, and our current device most definitely does *not* teleport."

[Full Disclosure: I asked for and received explicit permission to include the two sentences to come, despite the danger of leaks.]

"We've found what you might call a road, invisible to almost all detection, that links places with the same name. Almost as surprising, we figured out how to access and travel it."

CoSIP applications, as anyone authorized to read this filing will know, are often granted a patent without a working model. We wish to encourage inventors to speculate fairly wildly, we made the conscious decision to patent speculations, to reward daring thinking, to allow as many flowers as possible to be planted, perchance to bloom.

I've heard crazy, is what I'm trying to say, and I certainly would have put this farther out on that axis than teleportation. Not that I in any way believe in teleportation, I assure you – I'm not ready to be institutionalized just yet. I only compare the two to make clear how stunned I was when CTO Mosseri offered to take me anywhere in the world.

(CoSIP rules prohibit identifying details, even altered, for fear I will give away more than I realize. What I share here captures my personal experience; any reader who thinks I have revealed anything about the Israelis' device should be warned I have included many red herrings, at the Israelis' request. In addition, they have vetted this summary, edited in line with their suggestions, to remove all revealing information, adding dead ends as well.)

I cleared a day, they told me I would not need that long. They placed me in a remarkably light sensory-deprivation wrap, covered by another CoSIP patent, I believe. They led me – I do not know if we walked, rode, or flew, the cloak is that good – until I was in their device, meaning I do not know where they had it stored, how large it was or how we entered it.

Unwrapped, I found myself standing on a sort of platform, like waiting for a train, Metro, or subway, with the CTO and her staff. She said Bogota, a sort of dirt road appeared, we walked ten paces. I closed my eyes and was again enclosed; when they unpeeled me next, the drama of the moment and leftover effects of sensory deprivation convinced me I would be in Colombia.

Instead, I found myself on the streets of a small town in New Jersey, struggling to maintain its population of eight thousand. Mosseri laughed in delight at my face, said she probably had the same look for her maiden voyage. It was a flourish of the inventor(s) – all details of whom are carefully guarded, for his/her/their safety.

Best I can figure from the flow of the conversation, mostly a wild guess, the core idea came to one, both, or all the inventors as children, s/he/they saw the name Bogota on a street sign in the back seat of his/her/their parents' car driving around New Jersey, wondered how the capital of Colombia had moved to New Jersey.

To anticipate the kinds of questions you like to ask when I submit my reports, ma'am, yes I did point out this information offers a clue to identity. The CTO smiled and agreed, said more than two million Israelis hail from the Tri-State or lived there a year or more of their childhood. She wasn't worried.

To honor the original inspiration, they rigged the machine to take all first-timers to Bogota, NJ. She asked me if I was ready for the next stop, I said yes, we did the routine again, sensory deprivation, subway platform, she said Bogota again. Twenty paces later, freed to see, I was on the streets of Bogota, Colombia.

Sufficient proof supplied, this examiner grants the application. Any similar devices built in the next twenty-seven years must show a conceptual difference from Israel's, or pay royalties.

I also recommend a delay on the clock on this patent, as the device has kinks. For a simple example, it took us seven brief walks on the return trip to Oslo. I asked why we could not go back to Bogota, NJ, and then here, or come straight to Oslo. They said they could not explain without giving up too many secrets.

Forty-four minutes of walking to go from Bogota to Oslo still beats current transportation (I did not ask about costs; as my supervisors have reminded me too many times, we at CoSIP are not concerned with financial viability). I empathize with their desire to have a version which can meet the needs of their least ambulatory customers before their patent begins to run, and urge the full court to agree.

Details for comparison purposes: In the unfortunate case of a patent infringement lawsuit, detailed plans of both devices would need to be studied in a secure location. The patent holder prefers to avoid the possibility as much as possible, given human nature and leaks.

To help forestall time-sucking nitty-gritty arguments about similarity, this application includes a few extra details, to help courts dismiss as many challenges as possible.

The Israelis assert under oath their device includes all place names, down to specific buildings, on any current map, updated daily by secure Interweb sweep. Competitors should not be granted alternate patents based on a supposedly larger database.

The device prides itself on its simplicity, and the Israelis have licensed the rights to the slogan "a minute to learn, a lifetime to master," from the game Othello, licenses and copyrights duly registered and renewed with our sister body, the International Patent Office, in Beijing.

Ease of training, too, cannot ground a parallel patent.

Addendum: For reasons they chose not to share, the CTO and her staff contacted me about two weeks after our original meeting, to say they now believed they were ready for street-level, public patrons' tests later this year, and therefore withdrew their request for delayed patent installment. Twenty-seven years, starting... Now.

FORBES Insider Tip: SWaTCO

Congratulations *FORBES Insider*, for the good financial sense to invest a step beyond *FORBES PLUS*! Today, your membership brings you early first word on a company called Small World Travel, out of Israel, which has almost definitely not hit your radar [if it has, send us your resume, we're always hiring!].

Today's tip gives you the information we have on a company whose upside claims go beyond anything we've seen in a long time. The buzz is just starting to develop, and beating the buzz means money, we always say.

Here's what we know, with thoughts on the best ways to reap a profit. Because here at *FORBES Insider*, we're not satisfied to offer inert information, as if you have the time or expertise to know how to translate it into action. We know you're busy, it's why you pay us.

Admittedly, someone's shut the lid tight on this one. The most our contacts have been willing to share, even off the record and despite our great history of protecting confidentiality, tells us SWaTCO will disrupt travel more than any of the celebrated industry upheavals of the past, bigger than the printing press or the early Internet.

The passenger airline and long-distance train industries have three to five years before they're curiosities for history buffs, we hear, bus and commuter rail to follow soon thereafter, automobile usage to drop by a quarter, maybe as much as fifty percent or more. Cargo transport is still safe, but they're working on it.

We don't know how, and rumors of revolutions have failed to pan out in the past. We do hear word of a CoSIP patent granted and running. They're close to market, in other words, now's the time to jump in, ahead of the curve. Yes, jump into we don't know what.

Word out of CoSIP says this is not a train to miss – just our having been contacted tells you how big it is, *no one* leaks from CoSIP, it's the most zealously tight-lipped body we ever run up against, top ten for security, background checks, secrecy oaths, and penalties for breach. CoSIP employees are dedicated, first and often last, to CoSIP.

Question for you and us always is, how do we make money off this news? Easiest play would be company stock, obviously; unfortunately, they seem to have deep enough pockets to stay private, no stock or angel investors, Israel's government owns it on behalf of the citizens, our sources say. No way to buy into that, either, corruption over there's never recovered from Sar Shalom's honesty crusade.

The next option also won't work, finding allied businesses, or businesses in towns likely to see a SWaTCO boom, such as Beersheba, where they're based. All those companies list on the Tel Aviv exchange, closed to all non-residents of Israel for fifteen years now.

Nope, not closed to non-Jews, readers have made that mistake before, we've had a few complaints from people who skimmed the article, converted to Judaism planning to buy into the Tel Aviv exchange, then found out their mistake. Israeli government press people asked/required we add warnings every time this kind of situation arises.

First, the government wants us to warn you about any too-easy option to become Jewish, conversion courts that tell you they can do some mumbo jumbo, make you Jewish in less than six months. Doesn't work, you'll be no more Jewish than before. The government begs anyone interested to make sure they find a reputable court (yes, that's a PSA for the Israeli government; we publish there, too, part of the deal is to be good citizens, play ball occasionally).

Insult to perjury, conversion doesn't do it. Best conversion in the world, the Tel Aviv exchange is open to residents only. And you don't have to be Jewish to be a resident, either (for details, go to the Israeli government site, under "Emigration to Israel.")

For a score this big, of course, you might be tempted to move, establish residence, invest, wait the five years, cash out, and go. Despite our usual policy against making radical life changes in the hopes of an investment windfall, SWaTCO's juice might very well be worth the squeeze.

If you're close to retirement and behind on your nest egg, for example, here's the home run you were hoping would drop in your lap. Besides, after a year of residence or purchase of a home, you're included in a great social services network [careful: with the purchase comes an oath to reside there for seven months a year for five years, and they take oaths *very* seriously.]

Now the caveats. They enforce extensive morality obligations for non-Jews, more intrusive than here in the West, and Jews must observe the religion in all public ways, including not violating the Sabbath, holidays, or dietary laws. Handle that seven months a year for five years – and don't be obvious about violating it when you're out of the country – our sources say you'll be set for life.

Full disclosure: our CoSIP leaker funneled word to us through intermediaries, more than one of whom has chosen this option. Their portfolios have doubled and tripled just in the time SWaTCO's been developing whatever it develops.

Here's a wrinkle, though: Many of them have told us they don't plan to leave after the five years now that they've lived there, and aren't telling us anything more. We worry it might be a bait and switch, suck you in, don't let you out scenario, we don't want readers misled. Forewarned is forearmed.

For those of you who join us in caring about freedoms and rights, here's an idea less enmeshed with Israel itself. Look for companies who stand to benefit from SWaTCO's moves. Some Israeli companies provide support to SWaTCO's technology and list on exchanges outside Israel, and some Israeli localities sell bonds in non-Israeli markets.

Good example: International Staffing, a year-old unicorn-to-be, supplies human resources, cultural training, new employee absorption and retention for Israeli corporations abroad. As SWaTCO rolls out whatever, bet on International Staffing to ride those coattails.

For bonds, we like the small towns south of Beersheba, poised for breakout growth as soon as they find a foundation of an economy. Sde Boker has a bond offer in London, Dimona in Toronto, and Mitzpe in New York. Hard to pick the winner among them, best to buy them all.

Not convinced enough to take a stab at the future of a foreign country's plans? Try shorting the airline industry, a quick in and out, each time SWaT-

CO makes a move, the jittery markets will nosedive. You might do it multiple times, actually, short the peaks, sell the dips.

Longer-term and slower to fruition – ultimately more productive, we believe – find municipalities *outside* Israel most likely to benefit – cities, towns, hamlets, with common names, we hear. Buy up property in all the Springfields, on Main or Park streets, they'll be the new travel hubs. Six degrees will take you from one place to another, commonest names will see the most traffic.

Or, if you're exceptionally entrepreneurial, time on your hands, open a business in one of these places, caters to travelers. Who doesn't want coffee first thing after a trip?

Legal disclaimer time. As always, any of this might change. All new technologies hit snags, roll-outs always find unanticipated problems. Choose well, stay alert, moment to moment. Revolutions are gold mines, as long as you work at it. We'll update you as more information becomes available. Good luck and happy hunting from your friends at *FORBES Insider*!

Wharton School, University of Pennsylvania, Form 85729863, Withdrawal Request

Withdrawee: Jack Atid Turner, 3rd year student, 30 credits shy

Length of Withdrawal/ Fee Waiver: I plan and hope this will be permanent. I am withdrawing for an exciting opportunity, one I believe will either last or lead to a stream of follow up jobs, where I'll work and move until a degree will no longer matter. I am not yet there, and therefore need a fee waiver, who can spare half a year's tuition?

Reason for Withdrawal (Please Attach All Relevant Affidavits of Medical or Psychiatric Need, Contact Information for any Substance Abuse Facilities): Thank God, no, nothing like that. I have been offered better than I deserve, the ground-floor of a future I did not realize was my dream until it came knocking. I can't say too much, confidentiality agreements and all. What a hoot, someone asked *me* to sign a confidentiality agreement!

I can say I've been offered a job with SWaTCO, employee *fifty*, number two on the team handling rollout for the US, their first foreign market. My boss, a great mentor, came out of retirement, means the job is mine down the road if I can prove myself, puts me in the pole position for leading expansions to the rest of the world.

The attached *FORBES Insider* article justifies my decision. If SWaTCO is a third as successful as the early betting, I'll be set for life. They want me now, don't care about my lack of degree, say our degrees haven't been worth the tuition for a quarter century (sorry). I've met their bigwigs in person, they think I can do the job and make the kind of intelligent, cultured conversation important to convincing the leaders of countries to let us in.

"Keep reading thirty books a year from a range of fields, you'll be as good to us as if you did have a degree, son," said my new boss.

I attach the formal job offer from SWaTCO HR.

Additional Comments: Dean Whetmyckker, I appreciated the time you took to speak with me after my student advisor made such a mess of it. I'm putting as much in writing as I can, as you asked. I hope you'll keep to yourself anything else we may have chatted about.

For the purposes of the document trail you need to justify approving my withdrawal, I can add this: during my time at Wharton, you did us the favor of inviting other students who withdrew to come speak about their successes and challenges, and my opportunity seems better than anything they discussed, a higher upside, lower risks. They've all ridden theirs to "lifetime financial stability," our top goal at Wharton.

SWaTCO is like a startup in its advantages, stock options, bonuses based on what I am happy to bet will be significant growth. With the safety net of the Israeli government as partners, a government that has run in the black for the past twelve years, with a commitment to taking care of hard workers.

Worse comes to worst, we fall on our faces – not a real possibility, I've met the people up the chain of command, not a one of them fall on their faces types, nor am I. I'm keeping the door here open only because Wharton always taught us to imagine the worst as part of our process, and the *worst* is I walk away with nothing. Honestly, I don't believe it; His New Majesty's government takes responsibility seriously, would almost definitely give us jobs in the public sector if this goes belly up somehow. A career there doesn't seem too bad a nightmare scenario.

I know it's not master of the universe, like I promised I would become in my application; I found out I can live with that. Happily. I give it a shot and it goes south, nothing ventured, nothing gained, better to have loved and lost and all those other nostrums you guys teach us.

Now, here's the story you asked me to write up. I just need to remind you of your promise to file it securely, share it only with select struggling students. My new boss agreed, as long as I put my limits on the record.

The moment I came to my decision is what you asked, right? You remember my mom's been reporting from Israel, right? Couple weeks ago, I took a long weekend to visit her, just after Knesset selection, she was wondering whether ABC would extend her assignment, to cover the early stages of the new government, was worried about her job security.

I had no good reason to suddenly travel across the world to see her. We'd been apart two weeks plenty of times. Knowing she was thousands of miles away instead of a two-hour drive, first time in years, bothered me. She's not getting any younger, a voice said inside of me.

I called to ask permission, because it costs money, you know? And I knew she gave and gives up a lot to keep me in school. Anyway, she said sure, come on over.

Israel today, life shifts tracks Friday night and Saturday. The weekend I went was the first of the campaign to fill the three slots at the top of the pyramid. My mom wangled us invites to a small town in the Etzion bloc, where Sophia Mosseri lives.

Yes, the new CTO. Trust me, after two hours with her, you'd know Chief Technology Officer of the Messianic Kingdom of Israel is the least impressive line on her resume. I thought *I* was a go-getter, when every interest I had, every hobby I'd taken up, she was on top of it, seemed like she knew it better than me, before we got around to how she spent her days.

The fifth time she knew about an odd hobby of mine – badminton, as it happened – I wondered aloud how she found the time, she laughed. "First, young man, I have sixty years on you, more chances to dabble in this and that. Secret two, I'm a dabbler.

"I do enough of an activity, study enough of a subject, to discuss it intelligently, if superficially. I get bored, it's my weakness, I don't have the resolve – no, not the right word, I want to say stick-to-it-ness, no, not grit, it's different – to see it through.

"When *I* was a kid, people denigrated jacks of all trades, said they were masters of none. With disdain, as if any person of good self-discipline could, should, and would suck it up, keep their nose to one grindstone only, learn what they needed to become an expert, and then live. Wasn't how I could work, and it took me too much time, pain, and tension in relationships before I admitted it.

"I had the great good fortune to choose parents who supported me while I found myself. Gave me the wings to start a company at nineteen instead of shoehorning myself into some professor's set curriculum.

"After we went unicorn, I sold it to people I knew could grow it, kept a quarter for myself, did it again, and again, and again. The ideas, they never stopped coming, all I needed was people to pick up where my limited interest petered out. Eventually, starting new companies started to feel humdrum, too, a pattern I had mastered – have the idea, find the barriers, cajole the right people into taking a break from their success train, join me to solve the problem, go public, make a mint. Repeat.

"I turned to non-profits, a *much* harder nut."

A half hour with her was like a master's class in what we're learning here at Wharton, worth way more than the cost of the plane ticket, and the weekend was far from done. I'd seen my mom, heard a great origin story, made a contact, found hope I could find a place in the world whether or not I fit at Wharton (thank you, Dean Whetmyckker, for your positivity, it's been a tremendous help at my lowest, but let's be serious, I *don't* quite fit).

Three festive meals and two long group walks later, I had met too many people to list. No one stood out, it was the tidbits they dropped, fascinating, thoughtful, successful people, each gave me a jigsaw piece or two to patch together my future. It was like a 25 hour retreat with the best professors, all dedicated to spending time with you.

(An idea for Wharton to consider, sir, for current students or laypeople. At a premium price, of course – pick a locale, or better, sell one or two people at a time the right to shadow a prof for a week, as s/he conducts his/her side businesses, sit with them in pre – and post-mortems about deals in progress or contracts signed, I bet they learn as much or more as their classes).

Greatest weekend of my life already, I'm not up to the best part. In Israel, the Sabbath ends with a ceremony, name doesn't matter, it includes a tall candle, singing, swaying, you get the idea.

The man reciting the prayer puts out the candle and CTO Mosseri says to me, "Atid (my Hebrew name, people there prefer it, it means future, they like the idea), why don't you stay and work with us?"

Are you kidding me? A *job*? On the staff of a woman about to step into one of the three top jobs in the country? Where do I sign? I had to stop myself from sounding overeager, counted to five between each word as I stammered out a yes. If you read a transcript, you'd say I slathered it on thick in praising her. I promise, I meant every word, not an ounce of exaggeration in the lot.

She laughed. "Young man, don't sell yourself short. You're not going to be anyone's assistant. Besides, there is no opening at that position. My assistant is my secret weapon, my Meshullam here (her husband, a short, thin man, unremarkable other than her pulling him to her as she said it), the wizard of my staff. Thank Gd he has no interest in getting the credit he deserves, nor in pursuing his own ideas. Because if he did, he'd be me, and I'd be nursing my first or second start-up, waiting for break-even.

"Nope, I have a more interesting proposition."

SWaTCO. That's pretty much all I am allowed to tell you, although I promise I'll call you as soon as and each time any more is declassified.

I hope you understand this move reflects nothing about my feelings about Wharton, or takes away from how much I've enjoyed my time there, how much I've learned from everyone. In fact, I will be searching for US staff fairly soon, I hope you'll allow me to make offers to Wharton faculty and students (including you, if you're in the market).

Approval, James Pennybaker Whetmyckker, Dean: Approved, fee waived.

Added Note, Eyes Only: Karen, this is fine, don't sweat the money. We make nice with him on his way out, I bet we make it all back, with interest, in five years (please remind me to bring this up next board meeting, abolish the waiver fee, all it does is leave a bad taste, these are people leaving anyway, many going off to build generational fortunes, would include us if we were nicer about it, we're losing years of donations to sit back and enjoy).

Also, pls check fr spelling, send to young Tucker: "Jack, congratulations! I guess you learned Wharton's biggest lesson, it's not what, it's who. Still, lots of us don't know how to open the door when opportunity knocks. Of *course* we've waived the fee, and we hope you always remember you have a second home here. I'd say re-enroll if it doesn't work out, but I'm with you, you're on your way, something goes south at SWaTCO, something else will come your way. A special few of us don't need degrees, young man, you're showing yourself to be one.

If you're ever around Wharton (or, if the rumors are true, no need to confirm or deny, I'm not fishing, if you're ever near a place with a name *like* Wharton's, or like Philly, or on a street with any of the names here), I'd love to catch up. Or I'll come to you, keeping connections alive puts some fun in my job. Good luck, all the best."

And Karen, let's fill his slot, pls send me the first five names on our wait list, I have to figure out who has the means to plunk down full tuition and become a top donor in ten years, sell her to Admissions. Put the coffee on, stir in some extra sugars, it's going to be a long night.

Reuven HaOzer's Letter to Board and Shareholders, May 6, 2048

Dear Members of the Board of Temple Grounds, Inc., dear shareholders, dear all who believed in and supported me as I learned to crawl, walk, and run a service business, how to expand it without reducing quality, all people I am proud to consider friends:

I think we all knew this day would come. We are not a people whose founders lead us to the Promised Land, they drop us off slightly before – are any of us better than our Master Moses?

I had thought I would be different, as I said in last year's annual letter. I was sure this was my last stop, I'd be at the Grounds, happily, for another thirty, forty years, before I faded into retirement. I had visions of being that old guy behind the counter who's seen it all, who's telling new customers what their great grandparents ordered on their first date.

I hadn't been sitting on my laurels or coasting, either, I promise you, I was toying with versions of expansion, rolling them around my head, waiting for the name of the next store – it's not like I'm walking down the street every day and the right name pops into my head. Thinking of maybe taking the franchise abroad (might still happen, keep reading).

Before I share the news behind this letter, let me repeat how much I've cherished my run with the Grounds, I don't want it overshadowed. Our little baby, grown to young adulthood, has pushed *me* to grow, too, day after day. I owe the Grounds – and all of you who helped make it possible – my change from a guy who loved coffee, thought of a pun, and started a store, to a certified counselor. I owe the ways I've learned to be sensitive to others, alert and open to their problems, failings, foibles, and challenges, to the Grounds. Any services I have or will perform for others are thanks to your support.

It has been my privilege to shepherd our little project, the original, the four branches, the dedicated staff – including the temps or short-termers who left their marks on our stores and our hearts – as we have progressed or paused for breath, maybe occasionally taken a few steps back, found ways to pick ourselves up and have back at it. With over 200,000 served, I flatter myself we are treasured for more than our unbeatable muffins, I hope and believe we have made many lives easier in large and, more often, smaller ways.

Now, I've been invited to break out of my comfort zone again, in a way whose exact parameters I am not allowed to reveal. All the information I *can* share is in Her Honor our new Prime Minister's written offer:

"Mr. HaOzer,

His Late Majesty ob"m told HNM, on his deathbed, 'To me was granted the privilege and honor of redeeming our land and our people, to *you* falls the daunting task and great laurels of bringing the rest of the world to partake of the redemption.'

HNM has asked we who serve him to find ways to fulfill the mandate, and HNM singled you out as someone he expects to be pivotal to our efforts: 'Reuven HaOzer's time at the Temple Grounds, and his recent work with Ms. Tucker, prove him the person to spearhead the Palace's side of SWaTCO. We request you invite Mr. HaOzer to serve as Royal Liaison.'

In that light, please share this note with your Board and shareholders, and express to them our advance thanks – I speak on behalf of His New Majesty and my office – for their forbearance, for easing your transition from their company to ours."

I suppose I *could* refuse, except no one in his or her right mind would. It's too good.

My second piece of business is to help you replace me, less hard a task than those of you with whom I had casual conversations seem to think. You all know Shani Feinbaum, her name has come up in annual letters over the years, she facilitated many of our successes from His Late Majesty's side, helping with needed permits, greasing certain wheels, and the like. I nominate her to take over as CEO of Temple Grounds, Inc.

Leaks happen, I've already heard rumblings from some in our community, complaining the Palace is pulling a fast one, His New Majesty's taking me, dumping Shani on you. False. HNM would have been glad for Shani to stay on, he has made clear; the two have known each other for twenty years, she would have had a much more influential role than SWaTCO liaison.

His Late Majesty also praised Shani in his deathbed comments. He would have been Messiah either way, he said, a less successful one but for the joys of having her as a partner, her organizational skill, her ability to remind squabbling factions of a shared common purpose, her way of clearing the fog of disagreement to enable focus on underlying shared values.

HNM left the decision firmly up to her, and she opted for a new kind of challenge, test herself in the private sector, see how she does when not backed by the king's prestige and power.

Me, I think we know enough to give her the keys to our little kingdom already. She disagrees, wants you to have a fuller accounting of her motives. She has asked me to tell all of you – as she will herself, if you agree to interview her – she hopes a step away from the public eye will make it easier to marry, have children before it's too late.

A less pressured environment, she hopes, will leave room for a life. Trust me, less pressured in her terms will leave her plenty of time for the Grounds and all its expansions. I work hard, I do, but I've seen her life and I've seen mine, and there's no comparison.

Prime Minister Ushidi has allowed me time to train my replacement. It fits SWaTCO's schedule anyway, the early products will roll out slowly in Israel, and my job ramps up as we expand to the US and beyond. If Temple Grounds, Inc. can settle on a new CEO quickly, I will have all the time I need to share everything I know, Shani can tinker and improve. She's a quick enough study she would learn all I have to teach with ease in the time I have. Especially because the two of us have chatted about the stores over the years, she's not starting from scratch. You know I would never make a recommendation about CEO lightly or because I owe someone a favor, although I owe Shani many.

Nor am I leaving the Grounds behind – ethics rules do require a blind trust, but I have told the trustee of my continuing commitment to my baby, and those shares constitute the bulk of whatever finances I have. In other words, I have a financial as well as emotional interest in ensuring you all are in good hands.

You've trusted me with the company all these years, I thank you for trusting me now. Those of you who still have doubts, come in for a coffee and a muffin, we'll talk it out. I know His New Majesty will write a glowing recommendation letter, if that's what you need, much as it would be a shame to bother him.

My father, he should rest in peace, always told me to stay attached to my roots. The Temple Grounds have been mine for longer than I ever imagined, and my future course in life will always be a circle, The Grounds the starting and ending point, the home to which I always return. I thank each of you for your support, and look forward to many years of working together on projects of service to our families, our friends, our nation, and our Land.

With fondest regards and a heart filled with gratitude, Reuven HaOzer

Confidential, Eyes Only, ABC News/Entertainment

To: Shirley Beattie

From: Rachel Tucker

Hey Shirley, Rachel here. Life's weird, I know we've said it a million times in the break room, it's one thing talking about stories we're reporting, another when we *are* the story, right? Six weeks ago, I was sure Ryan had won, finally found his revenge for me turning him down for dinner ten years ago.

You always went to bat for me, I'll never be able to thank you enough; for all I know, there were more threats you quashed so well I never heard them. Then it got better, right? *I* got better, found my groove, developed an audience, learned to package stories in the way schools and teachers could turn into lessons on voting and democracy. I've gotten calls from think-tanks, too, who think these Israeli ideas about how to pick leaders might help restore US democracy to the city on a hill of yesteryear.

Honestly, a week ago, all I could focus on was how I'd made it this far, trying to avoid tasteless glee at Ryan's downfall, beginning to relax into the idea the network would keep me even after they brought me back home. I assumed my Israel days were limited, was going to plug away until the call came, wrap up a few personal situations (you know what I mean), and then get back where I belong, behind the camera, filming the glorious American heartland.

I know they've dumped parts of my job on you in this last while, too, I'm sorry for that. You being you, none of us heard a word, you just keep on truckin, I definitely don't say thank you near enough. I do love you for it.

I had this plan to show my gratitude rather than tell you, was going to volunteer for all your scut work when I returned, give you space to take extra vacation time or hours in the day to pick up a hobby. Or whatever. Because I owe you, and Jack owes you.

Best laid plans and all, I'm sorry to say. I'm attaching the formal request because, you know, procedure. I couldn't leave it at that, it was too impersonal. Still, telling it to you to your face felt wrong, like I'd be taking advantage of you, hitting you with hard news in a forum where you had to be polite and maintain your composure. Consider this an invitation to conversation, in person, handheld, however you want. I can be in New York with a day's notice, I want you to have the time to prepare how you want to react.

Because I'm asking ABC to suspend my contract. The new Minister of Public Relations/Foreign Minister knows a friend of mine, all right, I won't play coy with you, it's the least you deserve. The new Minister knows Reuven (long story short, still some bumps between us, not as bad as they had been, room for maybe a bit of optimism), and yes, considering how hard I find it to make connections, how jealously I guard the few I have, it's a part of what makes Reuven attractive, how easily it comes to him.

Anyway, Reuven sent Minister Orantal a mix-tape of stories I filed these last weeks, some you aired, some you didn't. The Minister invited me onto his staff, to focus on an exciting new project I cannot disclose, not even off the record, not even with a good friend of impeccable discretion. It's info crazies out there might torture you to get, and I'm not risking your safety.

Lem – Minister Orantal – did allow me to tell you the State of Israel will be expanding its footprint – *not* aggressively, no takeovers, military or other, he insisted I assure you – and whenever people move into new territory, mistakes happen. Enter Rachel Tucker, to do *hasbara,* as they call it here, basically make nice when material hits a fan. He likes my communications skills, I never tire of hearing people tell me that, a Gd's honest truth I'd only share with a dear friend. He says I'll be charged with, in his words, "helping the State of Israel recover from public relations fiascos quicker than if we stonewall, as too many of us have in the past." How can I turn it down, a chance to work with a new government on a new program, tons of upside?

You're literally the only one I'll be leaving behind, and I do feel badly, especially after all I owe you. Still, after sleepless nights, a lot of asking random bartenders for advice (by the way, a surprisingly good strategy; I'd never listen to *one* bartender, but when I averaged out fifty, their random good points helped alot), I think it's a step I have to take. I hope you can forgive me.

Here's the tricky part, and I know my accounts with you are low, I hope not empty. Can you help me convince ABC to suspend the contract rather than end it? I'm nervous, is why. Jack's out of school, has a job as good as mine, I think, tuition's no longer the point. Right now, anyway. I'm worried it might blow up, badly enough he doesn't bounce to his next startup, and I need the job for tuition again.

What does it hurt you guys anyway? If it works out, you never pay me again; as Ryan used to say, getting me off your bottom line will be a big help, for however long. And if I do ever come back (tail between my legs), I have to imagine the connections I'll have made in the Israeli government will be a help. I can be one of those talking heads with an impressive title under her face, former spokesperson, Israeli Government Special Projects. Right?

Thanks in advance, and certainly I'll give priority access, as much as I can, to whoever you send to replace me, so win-win.

Best to Paul,

Rachel

PS Here's the formal version, thx again, hugs and love.

Rachel Tucker Request For Leave Of Absence

As per reg 3A27WH, I, Rachel Tucker, hereby request an indefinite leave of absence from my duties at ABC News, effective two weeks from now (I can leave right now, I am offering the time to train whoever you're going to send, show him/her the lay of the land. After I leave the Israelis want me on board, and then I'll be limited in what I can do, conflict of interest and all that.). For the time of my leave, all mutual obligations would be suspended.

Reactivation of contract would be pursuant to a request by me, agreed to by the outside board of arbiters stipulated in my most recent contract.

Thank you,

Rachel Tucker

Reply To Leave Of Absence Request

Rachel,

Just saw this. You're right, I *was* banking on your return, a little more heavily than I realized until I found myself curled up in the little girls', face a mess and whatever. I'll be fine, don't worry about me, I'm not going postal or anything. Not today, anyway.

Maybe I'll quit, too, it's not like I have a college-age son, or a husband who needs my financial support, thank *God* I jettisoned Gordon all those years ago. Maybe I'll blow my nest egg on the surgeries I've wanted, drop Paul, bag me a rich man to take care of my old age. Hahaha, as if I could drop Paul, the man's woven himself into everything in my life.

In any case, all my problem, not yours. You found your out, congrats. If it's me still running this place after the network reacts, I'll certainly send the newbie your way – be ready for the greenest of the green, the way the budget here's being handled.

But. Yeah. Well. Leave of absence? Don't bank on it. My credit here was drained to give you the time in Israel you needed to prove yourself. No need for thanks, it was good for my job, too, just saying your recent success did not refill my tanks, there's no way they're going to be internally gracious about you finding your next rainbow to chase.

Like you said, some people here have wanted out from your contract for awhile, why should they be satisfied with maybe freedom, when they can get definite freedom? They know you're not going to turn down the Israeli government, who would?

Sure, the last few weeks you're all of a sudden again worth every penny and more. You know them, gonna take a lot more to make them realize they're losing a valuable asset. And they've made clear I'm not the woman to make them realize anything more about you.

End of the road for us, kid, you're on your own.

One last piece of grizzled veteran's advice before I go back to making paper airplanes while I ponder my options? Grab your gold ring, don't look back. You're gonna jump – you'd be crazy not to, I'd jump, and I'm way more cautious than you – jump with both feet. If you try too hard to keep a foot in the past, you won't jump as far, might fall into the abyss instead of reach the other side. Or however the metaphor would work to say it takes full commitment to succeed.

I'm saying go. Not harshly, callously, or without mixed emotions, I'm going to miss you like all get out. Don't worry about the contract, is my point, put ABC News behind you, a fond memory, I hope, and see where the road leads. Maybe our roads will cross again somewhere.

Good luck and much love,

Shirley

GOSSIP! MAGAZINE NEWS FLASH!

Atid (Jack) Tucker, newly of Nevatim (a small town near Beersheba, Israel) announces with pleasure and anticipation the engagement of his mother, Rachel Tucker of the Ministry of Public Relations/Foreign Affairs, formerly of ABC News/Entertainment, to Reuven HaOzer, Prime Ministerial Liaison to SWaTCO, founder and former CEO of Temple Grounds, Inc.

GOSSIP! readers might remember we called this a week ago, when Rachel – or, as we like to call her, The Rachel of International News Hotties – left ABC for a *government* job. Who does that, right? Stick with us, readers, *GOSSIP!* will keep you ahead of the curve. Read on for deets on our favorite former newscaster's planned nuptials.

In newly declassified information, the couple now reveals they met twenty years ago, while uncovering the Syndicate's attempt to corrupt the then-new Temple and disgrace His Late Majesty, then the new king, at the time known as Messiah only to Israeli Jews.

During their work together, they discovered the body of pregnant Rachel's missing husband, Elijah Tucker. Say more? No, sorry, the rest is still sealed, would implicate people who have paid their debt to society. Old sins should not hound us forever, Israelis say, someone's been rehabilitated, leave him alone.

Break their rules? We thought about it, except Rachel Tucker has shown us how much better off we are for knowing what's going on in Israel – that joint is jumping! Violating their confidentiality rules earns us a one-way ticket out, probably be another twenty years before we got back in to find out where they were leading us.

GOSSIP! contacted our favorite blonde former newscaster, she said no pictures, thanks, but her smile spoke volumes about the state of her head and heart today. Asked whether hindsight makes her wish she had stayed in Israel back then, saved herself years of loneliness and the challenge of raising a boy on her own, she ducked her head, laughed, and sighed.

"We'll never know, will we? Maybe I wasn't ready to give up the fun parts of life in the States, or wasn't ready to value the good parts of life here over the annoying parts – and there were more of them back then, too. I mean, I'm thrilled we've given viewers a positive sense of Israel these past few weeks, and it's all true.

"Still, like all reality TV, we also edited it carefully, my editors chose stories to make it a place our viewers would want to visit with us often. We de-emphasized other sides of the story, as do all storytellers.

"We backpedaled the religious monarchy, for example, we know it can be jarring to Americans, was jarring to me at first. I don't want to go too far the other way, they very much try to be gentle, work with people's individual religious struggles, but in the end, it *is* a religious monarchy, religion *is* required, the king does have lots more power than a president or PM.

"Not complaining, I promise, if I weren't excited about my choice, I wouldn't have made it. And I'm not putting up with stuff to be with Reuven; it all works for me, I'm heading into it clear-eyed and happy. Most of my fellow Americans, I think, would choose differently, upsides be darned. Or, if I'm wrong about my viewers, let me say it about me, twenty years ago: I don't know if I could have made it then. Stronger: I doubt I could have.

"It matters His Late Majesty Sar Shalom, may he rest in peace, spent these twenty years wisely and well, this country's a much easier place to live. Also, it's hard to admit your inability to take the bad with the good lost you twenty years of life."

Her eyes looked off in the distance or back at her younger self, and she shrugged. "Do I wish I had been a better person? Don't we all? Mostly, I wish I could have trusted in Reuven more, could have known what I should have, facing the future with him by my side would have meant we could handle whatever arose. Together.

"I guess we have to walk the path we have to walk, you know? It's like *GOSSIP!*'s letter writers always say, no use looking back with regret.

"I had twenty mostly wonderful years in New York, colleagues who made my life better every single day – I want to single out Shirley Beattie, a mentor and protector more than a boss. She's gone to bat for me, covered for me, picked up slack for me, the person most likely to have convinced me to stay in New York. Except she never would, because she knew this was better for me. Shirley, I love you!

"Also, twenty years of getting knocked around challenged me to pick up my game. Producing helped me understand people, the old me would have been too far behind Reuven's ability to heal others with his attentive presence for me to be able to live with it. It would have felt like living with a saint or a goody two shoes. He's still way ahead, I'm glad I've reached the point I can appreciate what he's doing instead of it raising the hairs on the back of my neck.

"Raising Jack, as *GOSSIP!* readers know him, on my own, built something in me, too, I hope character. Would it have been easier with Reuven? You bet. Unless I wasn't ready. Would have been ironic if I took the plunge then, my fearful withdrawing split us up, sent me back to the US, burned by reaching for a dream that wasn't yet mine to have.

"I can't change the past, I can and do hope I traded twenty years outside Israel, without Reuven, for many more with him, wherever life takes us."

GOSSIP!'s been speaking with Rachel by handheld, a voice says, "excuse me," the picture flickers, then widens, the call's been transferred to a desktop. Filled by a face we've all come to recognize and love from Rachel's broadcasts, Reuven HaOzer's.

"Don't let Rachel take all the blame here, I wasn't any more perfect than she was, wasn't any readier for the give and take of marriage. Proof is, if I had been, I'd have married. Not to Rachel, I know, she turned me down. I mean, I inhabit a country, religion, and culture strongly in favor of marriage; unless something in me was getting in the way, I'd have met someone else, not as wonderful as Rachel, we'd have made a go of it, and we'd have been doing ok.

"Looking back, I wouldn't say I waited for her – I believe I honestly had despaired of seeing her again – but someone or Someone was looking out for me. And here we are."

The Wedding

We know *GOSSIP!* readers want wedding details, and we aim to please! The location's private, almost a state secret, the happy couple tells us they want to keep it low-key. Rumor also has it His New Majesty Hazoniyah will play a prominent role. Rachel and Reuven did say the ceremony would be performed by R. Amittai Guvrin, whom you may recall from his solemn rendition of a Psalm at the late king's funeral. Reuven tells *GOSSIP!* Rabbi Guvrin's been a mentor for decades, particularly in structuring his coffee shops as spaces for safe conversations.

"When I wanted to give Rachel a clear-eyed picture of the difference between visiting and living in this wonderful, crazy country, we went to Rav Amittai. Making him the only rabbi with whom we both have a relationship, we're honored he will send us on our new adventure."

The Honeymoon: They just laughed and shook their heads when we asked. *GOSSIP!* suspects their new jobs involve a great deal of travel. Rachel and Reuven did tell us they had verified they would be assigned joint projects, liaising the different departments, and travel would be included.

"Leaving plenty of options for a honeymoon! My great friends at *GOSSIP!* and their readers shouldn't worry about whether Reuven's treating me well," Rachel said, with a smile. "For a year at least," she laughs, "we'll be in and out of Israel, a new city every week or even every other night, a whirlwind. But together."

Reuven piped in, "All that matters."

The Guest List: "Hey, we're simple people at heart. Rachel has a few colleagues who'll make the trip over, a higher-up or two who tell themselves she'll give ABC News more of an in if they make nice to her, her son Atid, I mean Jack, will be there, of course, and friends she's made here these last few weeks.

"For me, my Grounds family, five branches, full-time and seasonal, already puts the numbers up there. Then friends, like Shani Feinbaum, a few others, you know, nearest and dearest. Most of whom prefer to stay out of the limelight, and TIA to *GOSSIP!* readers and photographers for respecting our limits. Our own lives, welcome, part of the territory of Rachel's celebrity; friends and relatives, thank you for staying away."

The Date: May 15, a Friday they chose for the cutest reason: in Israel, Friday leads into the Sabbath, a quiet time, no electronics, away from the world. Then, this year the following Sunday night starts Shavuot, Rachel explained, another holiday, without electronics, ensures they have the space to focus on each other.

More important, the holiday celebrates beginnings, the start of the harvest season (*GOSSIP!* readers might remember the name from our May 2047 issue on how farming's roared back to life in Israel, provides twelve percent of GDP) and the Giving of the Torah at Sinai.

"We will link our new start to these other ones, in the hopes Gd will fold us into the blessings of the season, bless our harvest of the years it took us to find each other."

Amen to that, Rachel! *GOSSIP!* and all our readers wish you and your man the very best!

R. Yohanan Attarah's Address to the Triumvirate Inaugural

Ladies and Gentlemen, it is my honor to introduce the light of our eyes, our teacher in Torah, model of character, Most Revered Judge, *Nasi* of our Sanhedrin, R. Yohanan Attarah.

Please be seated, thank you for the honor you show me and the Torah. Quite a day, huh? Long one, too; I'm sure we're all happy to know our newest leaders have many thoughtful ideas on major issues. I'm also confident we had not realized how long it would take them to share their ideas as lucidly as they just did!

If I were you – and I've been you many times – I'd be sitting on my wrists to stop myself from checking my handheld too obviously. Three swearings-in, an introductory and acceptance speech for each, what's the running time on this event?

Yes, thank you, rocketing past four hours is correct. Although I *was* being rhetorical.

I've seen speakers make a point of calling attention to the lateness of the hour and then ignore it, use their full allotment, or more. We all know those people, who aren't willing to adjust or forego their prepared remarks to the exigencies of the day.

I hope I don't embarrass myself by now doing exactly that, as I may have done on occasion, and yes, I see those of you in the audience nodding in agreement. In any case, I have learned my lesson. Years of speaking last during deliberations at the Sanhedrin, after seventy brilliant colleagues have plowed the topic fully and deeply, teaches you to pick your moments.

Were my ego the only issue, I would have yielded my time completely, said thank you and good night, or made the briefest of congratulatory remarks to our leaders, Hashem should grant them wisdom, insight, and health as they embark on this exciting new era.

Honestly I would have, these last years have blessed me with ample opportunities to speak, to share my ideas, a privilege I do not underestimate or take lightly. It has freed me of the compulsion to speak for as long as I can any time anyone gives me a chance. Nor is this the venue for my usual talks, where we drill down into a topic for as long as it takes. The only reason I have not yet sat down is that social poison, rumors.

Rumors our Sanhedrin is miffed by His New Majesty's Knesset, feels threatened by it. Supposedly, we dislike the competition, fear a loss of power. I have begun fielding concerned calls and texts from relatives, friends, and acquaintances, in their most caring mode, checking I am all right.

A sad comment on us all, how easily we believe the worst about our Torah leaders, especially my colleagues – men more selflessly dedicated to Gd, Torah, and our people than any I have known. I feel obligated to speak up for them, despite how tired and antsy I know you all are. I will be as brief as I can; if I go too long, use your impatience to remind you to hate rumors, to commit to being part of their eradication from our society.

I speak to make clear we at the Sanhedrin are *relieved* at His New Majesty's absolving us of many political and legislative obligations. We have plenty to fill our plates, problems and issues we find intellectually thrilling, the kind of thinking too often pushed aside in the rush of the needed day to day decisions of a thriving country with a growing economy, expanding its world influence.

His New Majesty has done us a great *favor,* freed up much of our time to pursue what others dismiss as academic. In the sciences, they call it basic research, practical applications far down the road. We can now do the same with Torah, and we revel in our freedom to do it.

We of course will continue to advise as warranted, happy to do our part in building this country to ever greater heights. We will clearly sign off on any initiatives of our new Knesset, Hashem should bless their work with success, answer questions as asked, from HNM, other government officials, other courts. And we will speak up should circumstances force our hand.

We, each of us on the Sanhedrin, do still remember when we sat in a local court of three, the joy of helping people resolve disputes, restore good feelings, comity and amity. The Sanhedrin always had fewer cases reach all the way to our level, a sign our system works, cases being decided or resolved in a way no one feels the need to appeal. It has taken us decades, training judges in the wisdom of the job, a more delicate matter than the technical material of the law.

Now we spend most of our time on the backlog, the business no Sanhedrin was around to address for thousands of years. Temple laws were relatively neglected, sure, but so were many other areas. Great men have always tinkered here and there, found a loophole, constructed a fiction, head on consideration of the issues wasn't possible, because change wasn't possible.

It's not easy, either, figuring out what parts of the Torah Our Father in Heaven wanted to remain constant and timeless, what parts we are allowed or supposed to shape for each moment. We may be halfway there, we may be only a third of the way, I'm often too optimistic about our progress. Day by day, folio page by folio page, we're arguing it out, and having a blast. We meet in open session three days a week, you're all invited to watch.

So don't cry for us. We have jobs we never dared dream of having. Thank you, and congratulations again to our new leaders.

Our esteemed High Priest, Pinhas, has asked me to introduce him because, he said, he can trust me to stay away from flowery exaggerations. Let me only express our good fortune in finding a man of unquestioned caring for his fellow-Jews, a true and worthy descendant of our first High Priest, Aharon. May Our Great Kohen Pinhas inspire us now and for years to come. Ladies and gentlemen, my friend and master, Pinhas.

High Priest Pinhas' Address to the Triumvirate Inaugural

Thank you, R. Yohanan, my good friend. I shudder to think how much you'd have said if I hadn't exacted a promise to introduce me briefly! Ladies and gentlemen, as R. Attarah said, the hour is late, the afternoon sacrifice has long been offered, the sun sets, and many of us have been here since the Menorah was cleaned of its ashes this morning.

I, too, cannot forego my slot, for similar reasons to my friend and teacher in Torah. We at the Temple have also been beset by talebearers who see conflict where there is none, who think we priests, too, resent our supposedly waning influence. We join our brothers on the Sanhedrin in vowing we do not. Too many of our ancestor priests *did* use the Temple politically, we are happy to find the middle path by spending time leaning to the other extreme.

How do we fill our days, then, many have asked me, perhaps those who come to the Temple only on holidays, who are fortunate enough not to make errors needing atonement. If you're not there, you likely think the Temple's quiet. You'd be surprised.

First, we comfort every sinner who brings a sacrifice. It's not only an offering, it's a baring of one's heart and soul, and many sinners are upset and bothered. They believe in Gd's forgiveness intellectually, cannot muster the confidence Hashem will forgive *them*, are acutely aware of their failings, perhaps too aware.

Then there's the technical aspects, checking the animal, prepping it, and so on.

We do see fewer and fewer *sinners*, thank Gd and thanks to the spread and success of the Sanhedrin's educational programs. It balances out, the people who learn how to avoid sin also learn of the value of other offerings, daily, weekly, monthly, whatever rhythm works for them. Sin and guilt offerings are down thirty to forty percent, thanksgiving and peace offerings up close to the same numbers.

Years ago, people would visit Israel, become enchanted, buy an apartment, start with a holiday a year, then all the holidays, add a visit or two, and slowly spend more and more time, until they were living here. We find a similar pattern with sacrifices. Start with a thanksgiving offering for a Bar and Bat Mitzvah, move on to engagements, weddings, graduations, we at the Temple are, thank Gd, becoming an assumed part of every event, forming relationships with our fellow Jews, so they'll feel comfortable coming to us if (and when) they hit bumps in the road.

The biggest jump has been in flour offerings, by the way, not animal ones, for those who care about those kinds of issues.

Not to speak of the training. We have a five-year university for priests and Levites, and there is the simple physical task of staying in good enough shape to perform our services.

Finally, we stand available for His New Majesty. I have the privilege of wearing the *Urim ve-Tumim*, am happy to be the conduit for counsel His New Majesty (and/or advisers) may seek from Our Father in Heaven. I obviously cannot reveal confidences, I can tell you we are fortunate to have leaders who are not fooled into thinking the importance of their office says anything about them as people. May we all learn the lesson fully and well, for all our lives.

So, as my good friend said, do not cry for me or any of my co-workers at your Temple. We have our portion, are wealthy in our happiness in it. May we all occupy our places in this great nation with happiness and dedication.

And may Our Father in Heaven send His wisdom to Prime Minister Ushidi, CTO Mosseri, and Foreign Relations Minister Orantal, whom we are here to celebrate today. I am a) out of time and b) bound by rules of confidentiality, or I could supply ample proof of what good choices you all have made. May Our Father and King in Heaven crown their efforts with the pleasantness of His Presence, bringing it on all of us, for many years to come. Thank you.

Speech of Atid Turner at the Celebration Dinner for Reuven HaOzer and Rachel Tucker

Hi, everyone, thanks for coming. For the non-native English speakers, thanks for your forbearance. I thought about finding a translator or working with a coach to get me to the point where I could speak in Hebrew without embarrassing myself, my mother, and all of you. Then I thought the hell – sorry, heck – with it, how often does a son attend his mother's wedding, I wanted to enjoy it, not spend the time worrying about a twenty-minute talk at a celebratory meal two days later.

A joke everyone, a joke, no need for the nitroglycerin pill, Mr. Weiss, I won't be twenty minutes, dessert will come out in seven minutes. Or less if nerves make me speak faster than my dry runs in front of the mirror. I agree, I'm going pretty fast. Sorry, nerves. What, Mom? Yes, good idea, deep breath in, deep breath out, I'll slow it down. I only want the chance to share a word of Torah learning, as expected at these meals, and express my joy for Mom and Reuven.

This chapter in their romance took place mostly during what we call the Omer, the days from Passover to Shavuot, from the barley-flour offered on the second day of Passover to celebrate the upcoming harvest, and the two loaves of bread offered on the holiday we just finished – Pentecost in English, as it happens, but until recently, neither term meant much to me.

When I consulted Reuven's rabbi, Rabbi Amittai Guvrin, I guess now he's our family rabbi, I told him I wanted an idea related to this time period, laid out my limited background, high hopes to dazzle you all, to impress upon you how great a mother Rachel Tucker must be to have produced a speaker such as myself. The rabbi gave me more of his time than I had any right to hope, more Torah ideas than I would risk trying to share. I start by thanking him for his time and the ideas I remember, the ones I do not repeat here as well as the ones I do.

The one I felt I could tell you without going off the rails is from Ramban, whose name you all no doubt know. He was new to me; Rav Amittai, as he insisted I call him, told me he is called Nahmanides in English, lived in the late fourth, early fifth millennium. I don't live in the Jewish calendar, though, I had to look it up, thirteenth century in the U.S. calendar.

He said the business of Passover isn't complete until Shavuot. On Passover, we Jews left Egypt, were granted our physical freedom, on Shavuot, Gd gave us the Torah, our guide to spiritual freedom. He applied it to the flour offerings, too, but he lost me, sorry, R. Amittai.

Mom and I have taken a similar journey in this same short time. Not a lot of people know this, Mom was upset, no distraught, when ABC assigned her to cover His Late Majesty's funeral. Weddings are celebrations, I don't want to mar the mood by saying too much about Mom's attitude or mental state when she left the States those few weeks ago. See, my father, I should be an atonement for his repose – what? Oh, only in the first year? Sorry, I should have checked, what is it I say? Thanks – my father, of blessed memory, was killed here in Israel before I was born, she and I were almost killed a few months later, it was part of why she left, and the authorities at the time told her if she left, it was forever.

Going on air again was no joy for her, either. When you're young and beautiful, you think, hey, what's bad about the whole world seeing me all the time? I watched Mom age a little, get to the point where ten pounds can join at a moment's notice, stick around for six months or more regardless of her best efforts, or she'd wake up with puffy eyes immune to ointments, rinses, washes, cold spoons, or cucumbers. She wasn't interested in going back to sharing her physical ups and downs with the entire world.

I *certainly* wasn't happy about her going halfway around the world. If you're not from the US, you won't understand how primed I had been, from infancy, to think of college as *my* time to be the center of the universe, to be absolved of all worry or care while I did my thing. We pay enough, least ABC used to, and the limited window to build a career and a life creates enough pressure I'm not even sure I feel bad about how self-centered my friends and I were.

Mom being a couple of hours away was a big piece of the puzzle, the security blanket I needed more than I realized. A sudden assignment, ten years after the last time I'd had to put up with her leaving for more than five days, was not a happy event.

Listening to Rav Amittai, it hit me. Mom was taken from the US to Israel, just after Passover, when our ancestors were taken from Egypt, a land many of them loved, too. By Shavuot she had brought me along, both of us with exciting new lives.

Reuven was a huge part, my thank yous to him are why this makes sense to say now. Mom was too good a mother to drop even a hint I had been the reason she'd had to give up the man who could have been the second love of her life. I never knew Reuven HaOzer *existed* until a few weeks ago. But kids know when their parents are white-knuckling their way through life, know the difference between a happy parent and one determined to seem happy despite a gaping hole in their wants or needs, waiting for their time.

My first Shabbat with the two of them, I knew he was Mom's missing piece. Gd has made this a time for Mom and me to take the trek our people did long ago, and our hearts are full of gratitude for His leading us where we would never have found the way without a push.

I've been told the tradition at these parties is for well-wishers to address new couples by speaking heartfelt words to their relative, then say something like "I know the bride (or groom) better than I know the groom (or bride), but in the few chances/short while I've had to meet him/her, I've been impressed with..."

Clearly, I cannot do otherwise, I do know Mom longer than I know Reuven. Regardless, from the moment we met, Reuven has built a relationship with me, independent of Mom, for which I thank him. This won't seem like a big deal to any of you blessed with fathers growing up, but Reuven was the first person I met who knew my dad. Other than Mom, who never talked about him, said it was too painful.

Sure, over the years, I've run into elementary or high school classmates, I gathered great stories of him as a kid, memorized each one, deposited it in the vast abyss of a missing father figure. Didn't fill the hole, I wanted to know Elijah Tucker the man, Lije to all his friends – as Reuven told me he'd always say, rhymes with "eye". Reuven is the first person I've met who knew him after he moved 4000 miles away, to the life he'd always wanted.

I *could* have come to visit long ago, I bet many of you who live here are thinking, why didn't I? I think Mom was afraid I'd never leave, the connection to my dad's memory would be too strong. Turned out she was right, although not in a way either of us would have guessed. It was Reuven, he started telling me a few stories, pointed out places my dad had done this or that, I was done.

Not just stories, either, nope, Reuven knew my *dad*, what he stood for, cared about, the rocks on which he built his life, including of course The Rock Whose Works Are Perfect, Whom I hope I have remembered to thank. We'll never know how Dad or Abba would have evolved and grown, the man he'd have been today, but when I ask Reuven for advice, he's the first person I've known qualified to share a guess at what my Abba might have said. And share his own ideas, too, with a great batting average on good advice so far. It's early in the season, I know, easy to put up gaudy numbers, but I'm hopeful.

Two dads for the price of one. So as I ask you to join me to be upstanding as we toast the happy couple, I thank Gd, Hashem as you all say, for all the goodness in our lives, leading Mom and then me here, sending Reuven our way. Thank you, Mom, for being a mother who her whole life did her best to have me make my best possible self, thank you Reuven, thank you, Hashem. May we all share many more years of enjoying each other, fighting with each other, of growing, separately and together. Mazal Tov!

Coronation Address of Hazoniyah, King of Israel, ABC News Transcript

Ladies and Gentlemen, please rise for Our New Majesty, long may he reign, Hazoniyah .

Thank you, thank you, please, my brethren and sistren, take your seats, Gd's people should not stand a moment longer than necessary. Thank you, thank you. (Waves, points, smiles, mouth moves, words inaudible to our mics and lip-readers).

As a boy, my father, Our good deeds should foster his peaceful rest – with your permission, allow Us to apply the formula now in advance to each time We refer to him. Were We to say the words each time, may Our good deeds foster his peaceful rest, it would distract, yes? In addition, speaking here to the whole nation, whose faithful servant We hope to be, We hope you'll forgive Us for dispensing with the royal We necessary when addressing individuals or small groups.

My father, he liked old movies. This morning, as I reviewed these remarks for the fifty-seventh time, a scene from one came back to me. A famous actress (the character in the movie; the actress playing her was also a famous actress, a sort of joke within a joke) professes her love for a man, who runs a small, failing bookshop. In her pitch for him to set aside his worries over her celebrity, she says, "I'm also just a girl, standing before a boy, asking him to love her."

Or something like that, I was a kid, I haven't watched those movies in a long time; after he became king, my father didn't have time for diversions, the many needs of our great country swallowed most of his spare time. With his schedule and my growing independent life, whatever time we had together was also clearly too precious to waste on the parallel play of looking at a screen, interacting only with clever comments or plot predictions.

We did still see many movies, when the palace entertained artists of various sorts, part of hosting them would be to screen their work ahead of time, to have substance to back up our compliments. You buy a lot of good will by taking the time to engage with someone's lifework, Dad would say, goodwill he leveraged to all our benefit, in a way I can only hope to approach.

Until this morning, I'd have told you I had put those movies out of my mind, left them with Puff the Magic Dragon and the other detritus of childhood. Yet as I thought of what to say on this auspicious day, a day we hope and pray is filled with the good Lord's blessings, I thought of that actress, standing in a bookshop, aware of the difference between how the world sees her and who stares back from the mirror.

My next words might shock you a bit, I want to make clear I have checked their propriety with the teacher and master of all Israel, our *nasi,* R. Yohanan Attarah, and Our Honored High Priest, Pinhas, to be sure I am not belittling my office. As I stand here before you, coronated king of Israel, my mind fills with the thought I am also just a man, standing before a people, asking them to treat him as if he deserves the office, to give him time and space to grow into the shoes of the giant who strode this earth before him.

R. Attarah did tell me I should stop here to remind you Hashem has *obligated* you to treat me with awe and fear, regardless of how far you might outstrip me in personal qualities, wisdom, or good deeds. He reminded me I will be required to adopt postures to help you, will have to speak of myself only with the royal We. I – We, if you'll allow Us to practice a bit – will do so, happily, because Our father often spoke of how the office gave him room to do more for our people, our country, and Hashem's Torah, than as a simple Prime Minister.

In these last moments before I become Your Majesty for the rest of my life, before the needs of the country require me to exude the majesty of the office in all but the most private situations, I want to make clear I know it's about the office.

Some of you will encounter me where I am allowed to let my guard down. A bit.

Many of you, however, will see Us only in Our public role, Our voice dropped an octave, words spoken with the leisurely pace of one in charge of the room at all times, because We shall be doing our best to serve Gd and Gd's people by filling the throne with the solemnity, dignity, and austere impressiveness it deserves.

I fear it will be too little, I will not manage to evince the imperiousness needed. At the same time as I also fear I will become accustomed, will mistake the office for my right rather than my responsibility. I hope to make that harder on myself by saying loudly, for you all to hear, for me to remember, it's the office, and it's for you.

In the spirit of fulfilling the Mishnah's call to solicit much advice in order to gain much wisdom, We prepared for this speech by reading how world leaders across the globe and across history have introduced themselves to their people upon their formal ascent to office.

From what We found, from what We heard from the speechwriters We had Our staff call to check, leaders tend to lay out plans for the future. Were We to fall prey to the temptation, We would enunciate the direction We intend to take this great nation over the coming months or years, however long our Father in Heaven grants.

We have chosen to avoid specifics, on the advice of the brilliant team of advisers who have proven invaluable in these early days, who have already helped Us as king and us as a nation with their idea of elections; elections We think all agree were most successful.

Many say and perhaps think they want a monarch who takes the reins of the future and whips it into shape, as Our father His Late Majesty did. We have become convinced Our job differs, have come to believe We are meant to tread a different path.

It would be easy to repeat his actions, formalize his ideas into received and unchangeable lore. Times change, my dear friends, our strategies need to change with them. Nor can any of us know, ahead of time, which will work on which occasions. Our father was fond of a story of a university president whose predecessor, on his inauguration day, handed him four envelopes, told him to hold onto them, to open one envelope only when an insurmountable crisis hit.

The first crisis arose, he opened the first envelope, found a slip of paper with the words, "Create a committee." He thought about it, realized there *was* a committee he could create, it alleviated the problem, and life resumed. A few years later, second crisis, second envelope, "Endow a chair." Reflection again showed a chair he indeed could endow and solve the issue. Third crisis, third envelope, "commission a study," and he made his way through.

For the fourth crisis, the paper said, "Prepare four envelopes."

In our times, life moves too fast, crises crash upon each other, large and small, in waves of too high a frequency, too short a length, for stock answers or any grand plan. The advisers who gave Us a way to create a popular government without violating the principles of monarchy agree with Our proposition here: We cannot be John Galt, that thinker of old who spent 80,000 words telling you exactly how Our nation should look.

We can and will initiate projects, after due consideration and consultation, and already have exciting ones to bring to your attention, as many of you involved with SWaTCO know. But We here want to stress Our interest in meeting each of your needs, as individuals, even as the nature of Our office pushes Us to focus on bigger pictures.

We will move forward, step by step, working always to increase and enhance the great success bequeathed by those who came before, especially Our father. We will seek and find partners for the many initiatives Our Late Majesty was working on to the moment his final illness overtook him, and commit staff to finding and implementing the best new ideas, such as the SWaTCO project many here have already been deputized to join.

These are exciting times, and We do not mean our words to imply We will be quiescent, passive, or reactive. I speak as I do to assure you – because Our many initiatives might make you worry I've forgotten – We will always have in mind, as Hashem's Torah is read to Us many times a day, We are also just a man, Hazoniyah, trying to serve a people, Israel, with no delusions of infinite knowledge or certainty the path We choose is always right.

We thank you all for coming, hope you enjoy whichever of the coronation celebrations you have been invited to join, hope to see each of you, however modest you think your position or circumstances, during the visiting hours Our adviser Reuven HaOzer suggested we institute. We thank Reuven for ideas neither We nor Our other wonderful advisers had considered, and invite all who have such ideas to share them, with Reuven's office, or with Us at these open occasions. We wish him and his new wife, whom most of you know as Rachel Tucker, much happiness as they help us with our rollout of innovations.

This is the point in my remarks where speakers of our people would, for thousands of years, somehow segue into, "with the coming of our righteous Messiah, speedily in our days."

We are in the bittersweet position of being among the first to speak after the Messiah has come and gone to his just reward. We are left searching for a new phrase for wishing ourselves a great future. As We all join together, We here hope and beseech our Father in Heaven to show us the path to our next achievements, and to mottoes which will spring to our lips as the best way to close our conversations, speedily in our days.